Applied Management Accounting

Workbook

Aubrey Penning

Published by Osborne Books Limited
Tel 01905 748071
Email books@osbornebooks.co.uk
Website www.osbornebooks.co.uk

Design by Laura Ingham

Printed by CPI Group (UK) Limited, Croydon, CR0 4YY, on environmentally friendly, acid-free paper from managed forests.

British Library Cataloguing in Publication Data
A catalogue record for this book is available from the British Library

ISBN 978-1-911198-69-7

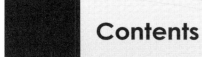

Contents

Introduction

Chapter activities

Answers to chapter activities

Practice assessments

Answers to practice assessments

Introduction

Qualifications covered

This book has been written specifically to cover the Unit 'Applied Management Accounting' which is mandatory for the following qualifications:

AAT Level 4 Diploma in Professional Accounting

AAT Diploma in Professional Accounting – SCQF Level 8

This book contains Chapter Activities which provide extra practice material in addition to the activities included in the Osborne Books Tutorial text, and Practice Assessments to prepare the student for the computer based assessments. The latter are based directly on the structure, style and content of the sample assessment material provided by the AAT at www.aat.org.uk.

Suggested answers to the Chapter Activities and Practice Assessments are set out in this book.

Osborne Study and Revision Materials

Additional materials, tailored to the needs of students studying this Unit and revising for the assessment, include:

- **Tutorials:** paperback books with practice activities
- **Student Zone:** access to Osborne Books online resources
- **Osborne Books App:** Osborne Books ebooks for mobiles and tablets

Visit www.osbornebooks.co.uk for details of study and revision resources and access to online material.

Chapter activities

1 Preparing budgets

1.1 From the following list, identify those responsibilities which may typically be part of the role of the budget accountant.

(a)	Authorise all capital expenditure	
(b)	Ensure that all budgets are fully coordinated	✓
(c)	Monitor budgets against actual performance and prepare reports on significant variances	✓
(d)	Submit company tax returns to HMRC	
(e)	Ensure that the budget timetable is followed by all participants	✓
(f)	Advise and assist functional managers in their budget submissions	✓

1.2 Complete the following table by using ticks to show into which budget each item of cost would occur.

	Cost of production	Maintenance	Capital expenditure	Marketing	Finance
Direct labour wages	✓				
Interest charges					✓
New computer system			✓		
Entertaining customers				✓	
Hire of machinery testing equipment		✓			
Raw materials usage	✓				

1.3   Complete the following table to show the forecast inventories and production units for a particular product.

Closing inventory should be 40% of the following week's forecast sales.

Number of Units	Week 1	Week 2	Week 3	Week 4	Week 5
Opening inventory	4,000	5000	4400	4700	4800
Production	11000	11900	10860	11100	11200
Sub-total	15000	16900	15200	15300	16000
Forecast sales	10,000	12,500	11,000	10,500	12,000
Closing inventory	5000	4400	4700	4800	4000

Forecast sales in week 6 are 10,000 units.

1.4   24,000 units of finished product are to be manufactured during October. Each unit takes four minutes to produce. Nine staff each work 160 basic hours in October. = 1440

The number of overtime hours required to be worked in October is   160

$$9 \times 160 = 1440$$

$$24000 / 15 = 1600$$

$$1600 - 1440 = 160$$

1.5   Department K manufactures three products, Alpha, Beta and Gamma.

Calculate the machine hours required to manufacture these in November, using the following table.

Product	Units	Hours per unit	Hours required
Alpha	190	1.0	190
Beta	200	2.5	500
Gamma	270	3.2	864
Total machine hours for department K			1554

There are three machines in the department.

Each machine can be used for 350 hours in November. Additional machines can be hired if required.

How many additional machines should be hired?   2

1.6 The following production budget for a month has been prepared.

Production budget	Units
Opening inventory of finished goods	5,000
Production	40,000
Sub-total	45,000
Sales	38,000
Closing inventory of finished goods	7,000

(a) Complete the following working schedule for raw materials. Each unit produced requires 0.75 kg of material. Closing inventory is valued at budgeted purchase price.

Raw materials	kg	£
Opening inventory of raw materials	3,500	7,000
Purchases of raw materials	32,000	64,000
Sub-total	35,500	71,000
Used in production	30,000	60,000
Closing inventory of raw materials	5500	11000

(b) Complete the following working schedule for direct labour. Each unit takes six minutes to make. There are 22 direct labour employees, each working 160 basic hours in the month. Additional hours are paid at an overtime rate of time and a half. The overtime premium is included in the direct labour cost.

60/6 =
10 units
per hr.

40,000/10
= 4000

4000 - 3520 = 480

Direct labour	Hours	Cost £
Basic time at £10 per hour	3520	35200
Overtime	480	7200
Total	4000	42400

(c) Complete the following working schedule for overheads. Variable overheads are recovered based on total labour hours worked.

Overheads	Hours	Cost £
Variable overheads at £2.00 per hour	4000	8000
Fixed overheads		12,000
Total overheads		20,000

(d) Complete the following operating budget, using information from the earlier tasks. Closing inventory of finished goods is to be valued at budgeted production cost per unit.

Operating budget	Units	per unit £	£
Sales	38000	4.50	171,000
Cost of goods sold:			
Opening inventory of finished goods			15,300
Cost of production:		£	
Raw Materials		60,000	
Direct labour		42400	
Production overheads		20000	
Total cost of production			122400
Closing inventory of finished goods			21420
Cost of goods sold			116280
Gross profit			54720
Non-production overheads		£	
Administration		15,000	
Marketing		12,500	
Total non-production overheads			27500
Net profit			27220

1.7   The following budget data has been prepared.

Budget data	June £	July £	August £	Sept £
Credit sales	8,900	8,300	8,800	9,500
Purchases	4,200	5,100	4,800	4,900
Wages	2,300	2,350	2,300	2,400
Expenses	1,050	1,080	1,070	1,090
Capital expenditure	2,000		4,500	

Timings:

4 980

60% of credit sales are received in the month after sale, the remainder one month later. Purchases are paid in the month after purchase. ✓

Wages are paid in the month incurred. ✓

Expenses are paid in the month after they are incurred. Expenses include £200 per month depreciation.

Capital expenditure is paid immediately as it is incurred.

Complete a cash forecast for August, using the following table.

Cash forecast – August	£
Opening cash balance	16,400
Receipts from sales	8540
Payments for:	
Purchases	5100
Wages	2300
Expenses	880
Capital expenditure	4500
Total payments	12780
Closing cash balance	12160

2   Using budgets

2.1 The following information is available about a company that makes a single product.

- Each unit is made from 1.5 kg of material costing £1.80 per kg.
- It takes 15 minutes to make each item.
- 800 hours of basic labour time is available in the month of April. Any extra hours must be worked in overtime.
- The basic labour rate is £12 per hour. Overtime is paid at time and a half (50% more than basic rate).
- Variable overhead relates to labour hours worked, including overtime.
- Fixed overhead costs are incurred evenly through the year.

Complete the following table with the April budget figures.

	Budget for the year	**Budget for April**
Units sold	36,000	3,000
Units produced	40,000	3,500
	£	£
Sales	540,000	45,000
Cost of production:		
Materials used	108,000	9450
Labour	122,400	10950
Variable production overhead	20,000	1750
Fixed production overhead	18,000	1500

11750

800 hrs ava
3500 units   ) 875 hrs
4 units per hr) 800 × 12 = 9600
                  75 × 18 = 1350
                          _____
                            10950

2.2   Calculate the sales budget, and the budgets that make up the cost of production for week 14.

	Budget for the year	Budget for week 14
Units sold	850,000	16,800
Units produced	860,000	17,000
	£	£
Sales	8,075,000	159600
Costs of production:		
Materials used	1,754,400	34680
Labour	2,720,000	53000
Variable production overhead	1,978,000	39100
Fixed production overhead	1,040,000	20000
Total cost of production	7,492,400	146780

Each unit is made from 1.7 litres of material costing £1.20 per litre.

It takes 12 minutes to make each unit. There are 3,000 labour hours available each week at a basic rate of £15.00 per hour. Any hours required over this are paid at an overtime rate of £20.00 per hour.

Fixed production overhead accrues evenly over the year.

2.3   Machine hire is a stepped fixed cost for a particular organisation. Each machine can produce up to 13,000 units in a year. The cost of machine hire is budgeted at £45,000 when annual output is 70,000 units.

Calculate the budgeted cost of machine hire for annual unit production of:

(a)   60,000 units

(b)   68,000 units

(c)   80,000 units

70,000 / 13000 = 6

45,000 / 6 = 7500

a. 5 machines = 37500
b. 6 machines = 45000
c. 7 machines = 52500

2.4   A company has already produced budgets based on its first scenario.

Assumptions in the first scenario:

- Materials and labour are variable costs
- Depreciation is a stepped fixed cost increasing every 15,000 units
- Energy costs is semi-variable, with a fixed element of £48,000
- Occupancy costs behave as fixed costs

The alternative scenario is based on:

- An increase in selling price of 2%
- A decrease in sales volume of 5%
- An increase in only the variable cost of energy of 3%
- An increase in occupancy costs of 2.5%

Apart from the selling price per unit, do not enter any decimals. Round to the nearest whole number if necessary.

Operating budget	First scenario	Alternative scenario
Selling price per unit	£11.50	11.73
Sales volume	190,000	180,500
	£	£
Sales revenue	2,185,000	2,117,265
Costs:		
Materials	541,500	514,425
Labour	570,000	541,500
Depreciation	182,000	182,000
Energy	124,000	122,366
Occupancy costs	203,600	208690
Total costs	1,621,100	1,568,981
Operating profit	563,900	548,284
Increase / (decrease) in profit		15616

Complete the alternative scenario column in the operating budget table and calculate the increase or decrease in expected profit.

2.5 The operating statement that forms part of the following table has been produced, using the original fixed budget (based on production and sales of 50,000 units) and the actual costs which occurred when 60,000 units were produced and sold.

Using the data in the operating statement, together with the notes shown below, complete the flexed budget and variances in the appropriate columns in the table.

	Original budget	Actual	Flexed budget	Variances Fav / (Adv)
Volume (units)	50,000	60,000	60,000	
	£	£	£	£
Sales revenue	2,250,000	2,640,000	2,700,000	(60,000)
Costs:				
Materials	600,000	780,000	720,000	(60,000)
Labour	750,000	895,000	900,000	5000
Distribution	200,000	255,000	240,000	(15000)
Energy	79,000	85,000	94,000	9,000
Equipment hire	15,000	22,000	18,000	(4000)
Depreciation	24,000	24,000	24000	0
Marketing	28,000	30,000	28000	(2000)
Administration	45,000	44,500	45000	500
Total Costs	1,741,000	2,135,500	2069000	(66500)
Operating profit	509,000	504,500	631000	126500

Notes on budget:

- Material, labour and distribution costs are variable.
- The budget for energy is semi-variable. The fixed element is £4,000.
- Equipment hire budget is based on a cost of £3,000 for each 11,000 units or fewer.
- Depreciation, marketing and administration costs are fixed.

2.6 The following operating statement has been prepared using marginal costing and a flexed budget.

Operating statement for November	Budget £	Actual £	Variance £ Fav / (Adv)
Sales revenue	96,000	88,000	(8,000)
Variable costs:			
Materials	32,000	30,000	2,000
Labour	16,000	19,000	(3,000)
Distribution	8,000	8,200	(200)
Power	6,000	5,900	100
Contribution	**34,000**	**24,900**	**(9,100)**
Fixed costs:			
Power	2,500	3,000	(500)
Depreciation	3,500	3,300	200
Marketing	5,000	4,500	500
Administration	6,500	6,500	0
Operating profit	**16,500**	**7,600**	**(8,900)**

The original budget was based on producing and selling 1,500 units. The company actually produced and sold 1,600 units, and the budget was flexed to this volume.

You have also established the following information about the operations:

- the quantity of material used was in line with the output produced

- employees worked overtime to cope with the additional output

- there was a change in both fixed and variable power costs imposed by the power supply company

- some non-current assets were sold for their book value; this was not originally planned

Select from the following statements, those that are consistent with the operating statement and information shown on the previous page and could form part of a report.

(a)	The sales revenue variance was caused by the difference between the original budgeted output and the actual output.	
(b)	The sales revenue variance was caused by selling at a lower average price than budgeted (£55 instead of £60). This may have helped increase the sales from the original budget.	✓
(c)	The favourable material variance could have been caused by either using fewer materials than planned or by obtaining the materials at a cheaper price, or a combination of these factors.	
(d)	Since the quantity of materials used was in line with the output, the material cost variance must have been caused by paying a higher price than budgeted for the materials.	
(e)	Since the quantity of materials used was in line with the output, the material cost variance must have been caused by paying a lower price than budgeted for the materials.	✓
(f)	A possible cause of the adverse labour cost variance is the need to use overtime hours, which are probably paid at a higher rate than basic hours.	✓
(g)	The labour cost variance may be entirely caused by the difference between the original budgeted output and the actual (higher) output.	
(h)	The changes in the power tariff have resulted in less cost overall for power than was budgeted.	
(i)	The changes in the power tariff mean that a greater element of the cost is fixed than budgeted, although the variable element seems to have decreased. Overall the total power cost has increased.	✓
(j)	The depreciation charge is decreased due to the profit on sale of the non-current assets.	
(k)	The actual depreciation charge is lower than that budgeted since some non-current assets were sold, and are therefore no longer depreciated.	✓
(l)	The overall operating profit adverse variance is mainly accounted for by the reduction in average selling price compared to budget.	✓

2.7   Unsure Limited originally produced two budgets, one based on an output of 10,000 units, and one based on an output of 15,000 units. The actual output (production and sales) was 11,500 units.

Complete the following table with a flexed budget and variances based on the flexed budget.

	Budget 1	Budget 2	Actual	Flexed budget	Variances Fav / (Adv)
Units	10,000	15,000	11,500	11,500	
	£	£	£	£	£
Sales	900,000	1,350,000	1,058,000	1035000	23000
Materials	250,000	375,000	299,000	287500	(11500)
Labour	350,000	500,000	380,000	395000	15000
Production overheads	170,000	195,000	190,000	177500	(12500)
Administration overheads	60,000	60,000	62,000	6000	(2000)
Operating profit	70,000	220,000	127,000	115000	12000

3   Standard costing – direct costs

3.1   A company purchases 12,000 kilograms of material at a cost of £37,800. The standard cost per kilogram is £3.20. The total material price variance is:

(a)	£0.05 Adverse	
(b)	£0.05 Favourable	
(c)	£600 Adverse	
(d)	£600 Favourable	✓

should = 38400
did : 37800
600

3.2   A company used 15,000 kilograms of material at a cost of £37,500. The production was 1000 units, for which the standard usage is 14,500 kilograms of material at a total standard cost of £37,700. The material usage variance is:

(a)	500 kilograms Adverse	
(b)	£1,300 Adverse	✓
(c)	£1,250 Adverse	
(d)	£200 Favourable	

should : 37700
did : 39000

3.3   A company expects to produce 18,000 units of Z using 6,000 labour hours. The standard cost of labour is £15 per hour. If the actual output is 17,500 units, what is the standard labour cost for this output?

(a)	£87,500	✓
(b)	£90,000	
(c)	£787,500	
(d)	£810,000	

17500

3.4   Radnor Ltd manufactures heating equipment. The company has several divisions including the
Radiators Division. You work as an Accounting Technician reporting to the Finance Director.

The Radiators Division operates a standard cost system in which:

- Purchases of materials are recorded at standard cost.

- Direct material and direct labour costs are variable.

- Production overheads are fixed and absorbed on a labour hours basis.

The budgeted activity and actual results for the month of November 20-3 are as follows:

	Budget		**Actual**	
Production units (radiators)		10,000		11,500
Direct material (paint)	500 litres	£2,500	650 litres	£3,120
Direct material (sheet steel)	30,000 sq metres	£45,000	35,000 sq metres	£51,200
Direct labour	4,000 hours	£48,000	4,100 hours	£51,250
Fixed overheads		£120,000		£120,000
Total cost		£215,500		£225,570

Calculate the following variances for November:

Variance		**£**	**A/F**
① Direct material (paint) price variance		130	F
② Direct material (sheet steel) usage variance		750	A
③ Direct labour rate variance		2050	A
④ Direct labour efficiency variance		6000	F

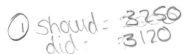

① should = 3250
did = 3120

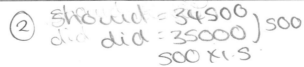

② should = 34500) 500
did = 35000)
500 x1.5

③ should = 49200
did = 51250

④ should = 4600
did = 4100
500 x12 = 6000

16   applied management accounting workbook

3.5   The standard direct material cost is based on using 0.5 kilos of material at £65 per kilo for every unit manufactured.

3,000 units were manufactured, using 1,560 kilos of material with a total cost of £99,840.

Prepare a reconciliation of the budgeted material cost with the actual material cost using the following table.

Budgeted / Standard cost of materials for actual production			£
Variances:	**Favourable £**	**Adverse £**	
Direct material price	1560		
Direct material usage		3900	
Total variance		2340	£2340
Actual cost of materials for actual production			£99840

3.6   The standard direct labour time is based on taking 6 hours to make each 100 manufactured units. The standard labour rate is £12.50 per hour.

5,000 units were manufactured, taking 307 labour hours with a total cost of £3,945.

Prepare a reconciliation of the budgeted labour cost with the actual labour cost using the following table.

Budgeted / Standard cost of labour for actual production			£
Variances:	**Favourable £**	**Adverse £**	
Direct labour rate		102-50	
Direct labour efficiency		87 50	
Total variance		195	£195
Actual cost of labour for actual production			£3945

4 Standard costing – overheads and sales

4.1 The following information has been calculated for the production of 1 unit of Zed:

- Each unit will require 12 kilograms of material at a cost of £8.50 per kilogram

- Each unit will require 0.6 hours of labour at a total cost of £9

- Fixed overheads total £200,000 and the estimated output will be 2,500 units of Zed

- Fixed overheads are absorbed on a per unit basis

Complete the standard cost card below.

1 unit of Zed	Quantity	Cost per unit £	Total cost £
Material	12	8.50	102
Labour	0.6	15	9
Fixed costs	1	80	80
Total			191

4.2 You have been given the following information:

- Budgeted fixed overheads are £700,000

- Budgeted output is 35,000 units

- Actual output is 30,000 units

- Actual fixed overheads are £680,000

The fixed overhead volume variance is £ 100,000 favourable / ~~adverse~~.

The fixed overhead expenditure variance is £ 20,000 ~~favourable~~ / adverse.

4.3   You have been given the following information:

- Budgeted fixed overheads are £80,000

- Budgeted output is 10,000 units and 5,000 labour hours

- Actual output is 8,000 units and 4,300 actual labour hours

- Actual fixed overheads are £85,000

The fixed overhead volume variance is £ | 16600 | favourable / adverse.

The fixed overhead expenditure variance is £ | 5000 | favourable / adverse.

4.4   You have been given the following information:

- Budgeted fixed overheads are £120,000

- Budgeted output is 12,000 units and 4,000 labour hours

- Actual output is 11,400 units and 3,950 actual labour hours

- Actual fixed overheads are £118,000

Complete the following table to show the fixed overhead variances.

	Variance £	A / F
Expenditure Variance	2000	F
Volume Variance	6000	A
Total Fixed Overhead Variances	4000	A

4.5 Complete the following table by ticking the relevant column to show whether each statement is true or false.

		True	False
(a)	The fixed overhead volume variance will always be numerically equal and opposite to the fixed overhead expenditure variance		✓
(b)	The net total of the fixed overhead expenditure variance and the fixed overhead volume variance is the amount of under or over absorption of fixed overheads	✓	

4.6 You have been given the following information:

- Fixed overheads are budgeted at £430,000
- Output is budgeted at 344,000 units
- Fixed overheads are absorbed on a per unit basis
- Actual fixed overheads amount to £419,500
- Actual output is 350,000 units

Prepare a reconciliation of budgeted fixed overheads with actual fixed overheads using fixed overhead variances in the following table.

Budgeted / Standard fixed cost for actual production			£
Variances:	Favourable £	Adverse £	
Fixed overhead expenditure			
Fixed overhead volume			
Total variance			£
Actual fixed cost for actual production			£

4.7   A company uses direct labour hours to charge variable overheads. The standard industry labour hours per unit produced is 0.5 hours, and the standard hourly charge is £3.50. During the month 10,500 units were produced, using 5,400 direct labour hours. The actual variable overheads for the month were £19,100.

Required:

Calculate:

(a)   the variable overhead price (or expenditure) variance

(b)   the variable overhead efficiency variance

4.8   A company uses machine hours to charge variable overheads. The standard units produced per machine hour are 10, and the total standard variable overhead cost per unit is £1.30.

During the month 20,250 units were produced, using 1,990 machine hours. The actual variable overheads for the month were £27,600.

Required:

Calculate:

(a)   the variable overhead price (or expenditure) variance

(b)   the variable overhead efficiency variance

4.9 Chippum Limited makes frozen potato chips from raw potatoes that are purchased from UK farms. The potatoes are first machine washed, and then put through a peeling and slicing machine where the chips are cut to shape. At this stage a quality check is carried out by staff who manually pick out from the conveyor system and discard any chips that have blemishes. The chips are then cooked, frozen and bagged ready for sale.

The company operates a standard costing system, and in September the following variances were recorded.

Variance	Adverse £	Favourable £
Direct material (potato) price variance	5,500	
Direct material (potato) usage variance	9,300	
Direct labour rate variance	1,200	
Direct labour efficiency variance	5,600	
Fixed overhead expenditure variance	1,000	
Fixed overhead volume variance	7,400	

The following information has been obtained about the operations during September.

- The recent weather has resulted in a poor potato harvest in the UK. The consequences include higher prices due to shortages as well as poorer quality potatoes with more blemishes than usual.

- The manual quality control operation involved increased hours and overtime working.

- The conveyor system was slowed to enable the more intensive quality control, and this caused mechanical problems, resulting in a break down which lasted several hours. A contractor was used to supply and fit the necessary replacement parts.

Write an email to the Production Director that suggests possible reason(s) for each of the variances, based on the information provided.

| **Email** |
| To: |
| From: |
| Date: |
| Subject: |
| |

4.10 A company that uses standard absorption costing has the following standard unit data for one of its products:

Standard selling price	£450
Standard direct costs	£180
Standard overhead costs	£230

During the month the budgeted sales were 5,800, and the actual sales were 6,000, generating actual sales revenue of £2,640,000.

Required:

Calculate the:

- Standard unit profit

- Sales price variance

- Sales volume variance

- Total sales variance

5 Cost management techniques

5.1 Dream Machines Limited manufactures motorcycles from parts produced in-house and bought in components. It operates one production line which incorporates automated and manual operations.

The company produces two models of motorcycle. The Rapier is a mass-produced model. This occupies the production line for 48 weeks of the year, based on 6 batches of 500 motorcycles each. The Custom motorcycle is produced to customers' specifications, and it involves six batches of 10 motorcycles each. These batches are scheduled in between the batches of the Rapier. The Custom motorcycle involves higher cost components and more labour input than the Rapier.

The company currently uses absorption costing, based on machine hours (i.e. production line hours). The production overheads total £6,885,000. Each motorcycle takes 50 hours on the production line. The current costs per unit of each motorcycle are as follows:

	Rapier	Custom
	£	£
Materials and Components	3,700	5,400
Direct Labour	1,000	1,400
Production overheads	2,250	2,250
Total cost	6,950	9,050

In order to change the production line from manufacture of one model to the other, the IT system must be re-programmed, and various tools changed on the robotic elements of the process. This takes an extended period of time, and it occurs a total of 12 times per year. The cost of these set-ups is currently included in the production overheads. The total cost of set-ups per year is estimated at £306,000.

It has been suggested that activity based costing could be used to deal with the set-up costs more fairly. As a preliminary exercise, you have been asked to calculate:

- The current absorption rate per hour for production overheads

- The absorption rate per hour for production overheads excluding set-up costs

- The cost per set-up as a cost driver

- The cost of set-ups per unit of each motorcycle

- The revised costs per unit of each motorcycle.

5.2   The following table shows examples of situations where different costing systems may be appropriate. Select the costing system that is most appropriate for each situation by ticking the relevant column.

Situation		Absorption costing	Marginal costing	Activity based costing
(a)	A private college that runs various courses. The cost of preparing learning materials is a significant part of the overheads of some courses, and the number of students attending each course varies significantly.			✓
(b)	A company that rents out holiday cottages that wishes to adjust prices so that late availability prices can be reduced without incurring losses.		✓	
(c)	A company that makes a range of different products using semi-automated production equipment. Some products are made in large production runs, whereas others are made to order in small batches. It is important that unit costs are as accurate as possible.			✓
(d)	A company that undertakes civil engineering projects that take a considerable time to complete. Nearly all costs can be attributed to a specific project.	✓		
(e)	A company that makes a range of products, each in separate factories. Since volumes are unpredictable it is important that break-even data is available.		✓	

5.3   Bullseye Limited uses target costing when developing new products. A new product is being considered which has the following cost and revenue information.

Sales	the demand is expected to average 5,000 units per month at a selling price of £7.00 per unit
Materials	the product requires 0.5 kg of material T for each unit
Labour	each unit requires 6 minutes of labour at £14 per hour
Overheads	the product would be manufactured in a separate factory, with total fixed production overheads of £10,000 per month
Profit	the gross margin required is at least 25%

Complete the following table:

Maximum production cost per unit	£ 5.25
Build up of maximum production cost per unit:	
Materials	£ 1.85
Labour	£ 1.40
Overheads	£ 2.00
Maximum cost per kilo for material T	£

5.4   Robot Technologies Ltd is considering developing a new product. It will combine driverless vehicle technology with mechanical robot technology to form a specialised vehicle capable of finding and repairing potholes in the road entirely automatically.

The following data has been collected regarding this new product.

Development costs (including creating prototypes) are expected to be £4,800,000 in each of years 0, 1 and 2.

Production unit numbers and sales numbers are planned as follows:

	Production	Sales
Year 2	100	0
Year 3	400	400
Year 4	400	400
Year 5	200	300

No production or sales are expected after year 5.

Variable costs of production are budgeted at £25,000 per unit. Fixed production costs are budgeted at £5,000,000 for each of the years 2 to 5.

Selling prices are planned at £80,000 per unit.

The company's cost of capital is 10%, and this is reflected in the discount factors given below.

Complete the following table to calculate both the non-discounted and discounted life-cycle cash flows for the product. Round to the nearest £000.

Year	Cash Inflow £000	Cash Outflow £000	Net Cash Flow £000	Discount Factor	Present Value £000
0	0	4800	– 4800	1.000	– 4800
1	0	4800	– 4800	0.909	– 4363
2	0	12300	– 12300	0.826	– 10.160
3	32,000	15,000	17,000	0.751	12,767
4	32,000	15,000	(7,000)	0.683	11,611
5	24,000	10,000	(4,000)	0.621	8694
	Totals		26100		13749

5.5   Delta Limited is considering designing a new product, and will use target costing to arrive at the target cost of the product. You have been given the following information and asked to calculate the target cost for materials so that the Purchasing Manager can use this as a target in her negotiations with suppliers.

- The price at which the product will be sold is £40.

- The company has firm orders for 10,000 units at a price of £40 for the first year.

- The fixed costs are £120,000 per year.

- The labour requirement is 20 minutes at a cost of £18 per hour.

- The required profit margin is 45%.

- The material requirement is 200 grams per unit.

(a)   Calculate the target cost per kilogram for the materials component of the product, using the following table:

	£
Sales price per unit	
Profit margin	
Total costs	
Fixed cost per unit	
Labour cost per unit	
Maximum material cost per unit	
Target cost per kilogram	

(b)   Complete the following statement:

The trade price quoted on the supplier's price list is £25 per kilogram. The Purchasing Manager has negotiated a discount of 15%. The discount should be **accepted / rejected** because the £25 reduces to £ [   ] which is **above / below** the Target cost.

(c)   The minimum percentage discount needed to achieve the Target cost is [   ] %

6 Decision making techniques

6.1 Tinnitt Limited, a canned food manufacturer, currently makes two products in its factory. The first is baked beans, and the second is garden peas. Both are sold in tins.

The following budgeted operating statement relates to the next year, and assumes that both products will be manufactured in-house. It is based on making and selling 2,000,000 units of baked beans, and 1,000,000 units of garden peas.

	£000 Beans	£000 Peas	£000 Total
Sales	400	220	620
Variable costs of production	120	80	200
Direct fixed costs of production	80	70	150
Shared fixed costs of production	100	50	150
Gross profit	100	20	120
Administration costs			40
Selling and distribution costs			30
Operating profit			50

Consideration is being given to an option to buy in ready made tinned peas at £0.14 per unit. This would save both the variable costs of production and the direct fixed costs of production of that product. Shared fixed costs of production would remain the same in total. The number of units of tinned peas sold would be unchanged.

If the decision were made to buy in the tinned peas, then the released manufacturing space could be used to increase the manufacture and sales of baked beans to 2,500,000 units, with some spare capacity remaining. The direct fixed costs of baked bean production would be unchanged by this. To cope with the increased total volume of sales, the selling and distribution costs would increase by £5,000, but administration costs would remain unchanged.

Complete the table on the following page to show a budgeted operating statement based on the position if the decision were made to buy in tinned peas and increase production of baked beans.

	Baked Beans	Garden Peas	Total
Volume (units)	2,500,000	1,000,000	
	£000	£000	£000
Sales			
Variable costs of production / purchase			
Direct fixed costs of production			
Previously shared fixed costs of production			
Gross profit			
Administration costs			
Selling and distribution costs			
Operating profit			

6.2 Beta Limited manufactures toothpaste and is considering launching an improved version to replace the current product. It will be sold in smaller packs since it will be most effective when less quantity is used.

- Current sales volume is 2.0 million units per annum and this is not expected to change.

- Current fixed production costs are £0.6 million.

- Current labour cost per unit is £1.05 which is completely variable.

- Current material cost per unit is £1.45 and is completely variable.

- Assume stock levels are kept at zero.

- Variable material cost of the new product will be £0.30 less per unit than the current toothpaste.

- Selling price will be increased from £5.50 to £6.00.

- Fixed selling and distribution costs will reduce from £600,000 to £500,000.

- Additional investment in assets will be £8 million which will be depreciated at £800,000 per annum.

- All other costs will remain the same.

Calculate the total annual increase in profit by completing the table below.

	Units	Price/cost £	Total £
Additional revenue			
Savings on materials			
Reduction in selling and distribution costs			
Additional depreciation			
Additional annual profit			

6.3 The following shows the standard data of one unit of product IFF:

	£
Selling price	22
Variable production costs	11
Fixed overheads based on production of 12,000 units per week	8
Total production cost	19
Profit	3

The product currently has UK sales of 12,000 units per week and no overseas sales. Capacity is 15,000 units per week.

A customer from Chile has offered to buy 7,500 units per week at a discounted price of £16 per unit, but will not accept a lower quantity.

Finished IFFs could be purchased from a competitor at £18 per unit.

Complete the following table based on accepting the order by buying in the units that cannot be made in-house. Insert zeros if appropriate. Make a recommendation as to whether or not to accept the order.

	Total per Week £	
Incremental revenue		
Incremental costs:		
Variable production costs		
Purchase of finished goods		
Fixed production costs		
Incremental profit / (loss)		
Recommendation	**Accept**	**Reject**

6.4 A company has already completed the following operating budget for the manufacture and sale of two products during the month of July.

Operating budget July	Product Xenox	Product Zenley	Total
Manufacture & sales volume	30,000	50,000	80,000
	£	£	£
Sales revenue	360,000	900,000	1,260,000
Variable costs:			
Materials	90,000	120,000	210,000
Labour	120,000	350,000	470,000
Contribution	150,000	430,000	580,000
Fixed costs			450,000
Operating profit			130,000

Both products use the same material, which costs £0.60 per kilo.

It has now been established that the amount of material available for July production will be limited to 250,000 kilos.

Required:

(a) Calculate the revised volume of manufacture and sale of each product in July that will maximise the operating profit from the available resources.

(b) Complete a revised operating budget for July, using the following table, based on your solution to part **(a)**.

Revised operating budget July	Product Xenox	Product Zenley	Total
Manufacture & sales volume			
	£	£	£
Sales revenue			
Variable costs:			
Materials			
Labour			
Contribution			
Fixed costs			
Operating profit			

6.5   A company makes two products, the Eff and the Gee, both using the same materials and the same labour.

The key details are as follows:

	Eff	Gee
Contribution per unit	£50	£30
Materials per unit	2 kg	1.5 kg
Labour time per unit	2 hours	1 hour

For the coming period, there will be a maximum amount of material available of 8,000 kg. The maximum labour available will be 6,500 hours.

Required:

•   Calculate the contribution per kg of material and the contribution per labour hour for each product, using the following table.

	Eff	Gee
Contribution per kg material		
Contribution per labour hour		

•   Using simultaneous equations, calculate the production of Eff and Gee that will maximise total contribution

•   Complete the following table to show the production, the materials required, the labour hours required, and the total contribution for each product and in total. Also show, for comparison, the production and contribution if the maximum units of only Eff or Gee were produced.

	Eff	Gee	Total
Production (units)			
Materials required (kg)			
Labour required (hours)			
Contribution			
Production (Eff units only)			
Comparative contribution			
Production (Gee units only)			
Comparative contribution			

6.6 Chippum Limited makes frozen potato chips from raw potatoes. The potatoes are first machine washed, and then put through a peeling and slicing machine where the chips are cut to shape. At this stage a quality check is carried out by staff who manually pick out from the conveyor system and discard any chips that have blemishes. The chips are then cooked, frozen and bagged ready for sale.

The manager has been investigating the purchase of automated quality control line equipment that would eliminate the need for the majority of employees. The purchase and installation of the equipment would cost £600,000, and would be depreciated at £120,000 per year.

The following statement of profit or loss is based on the next year's operation, assuming the current working practices, and production of 1 million packs of chips.

	£000
Sales	1,200
less:	
Variable material cost	300
Variable labour cost	250
Contribution	650
less	
Fixed production costs	100
Fixed administration costs	300
Operating profit	250

The net operating assets of the business are currently £1,600,000.

If the automated quality control line is installed:

- labour costs will reduce to £90,000 per year, regardless of the production level

- fixed production costs will increase by £20,000 per year, in addition to the depreciation expense

- other costs will be unchanged

The company's cost of capital is 5%, and discount factors over the five year life of the project are as follows:

Year	Discount factor 5%	Year	Discount factor 5%
0	1.00	3	0.864
1	0.952	4	0.823
2	0.907	5	0.784

The automated line will be paid for immediately and have no value at the end of the five year project. Assume that sales and costs remain at the same level for each of the five years, and occur at the end of each year.

Using the following table, calculate the net present value of the mechanisation project.

Year	Cash Outflow £	Cash Savings £	Discount Factor	Present Value £
0				
1				
2				
3				
4				
5				
Net Present Value				

6.7   A company is considering investing in a project that will require an initial cash investment of £3,000,000 to purchase non-current assets. The assets will last six years, with no residual value. The annual profits are estimated at £280,000, after charging straight line depreciation for six years. All profits except depreciation are cash-based.

The company's cost of capital is 10%.

Required

Using the following table, and any further calculations necessary, calculate:

- The net present value of the project using a discount factor of 10%

- The payback period to the nearest year

- The discounted payback period, to the nearest year (using 10% discount)

- The estimated internal rate of return to one decimal place

- The accounting rate of return to the nearest whole % (using average investment)

Year	Cash Flow	Disc Factor 10%	Disc Cash Flow 10%	Disc Factor 15%	Disc Cash Flow 15%
0		1.000		1.000	
1		0.909		0.870	
2		0.826		0.756	
3		0.751		0.658	
4		0.683		0.572	
5		0.621		0.497	
6		0.564		0.432	
Net Present Values					

7   Performance indicators

7 1   A trading company has the following results:

Statement of profit or loss for the year ended 31 December				
	20-8		20-7	
	£	£	£	£
Sales		209,000		196,000
less cost of sales:				
Opening Inventory	24,000		25,000	
Purchases	155,000		150,000	
Closing Inventory	22,000		24,000	
		157,000		151,000
Gross Profit		52,000		45,000
Depreciation	9,000		9,000	
Sundry Expenses	14,000		11,000	
		23,000		20,000
Operating Profit		29,000		25,000
Interest		2,000		2,000
Net Profit		27,000		23,000
Taxation		10,000		10,000
Net Profit after taxation		17,000		13,000
Ordinary Dividends	6,000		5,000	
Preference Dividends	2,000		2,000	
		8,000		7,000
Retained Profit		9,000		6,000

Statement of Financial Position	As at 31/12/20-8	As at 31/12/20-7
	£	£
Non-current Assets	130,000	139,000
Current Assets:		
Inventory	22,000	24,000
Trade Receivables	40,000	36,000
Bank	12,000	5,000
	74,000	65,000
Current Liabilities:		
Trade Payables	46,000	45,000
Short-term loans	0	20,000
Net Current Assets	28,000	0
Total Assets less Current Liabilities	158,000	139,000
Non-current Liabilities:		
5% secured loan stock	40,000	40,000
	118,000	99,000
Ordinary Share Capital (50p shares)	35,000	35,000
8% Preference Shares (£1 shares)	25,000	25,000
Share Premium Account	17,000	17,000
Revaluation Reserve	10,000	0
Retained Earnings	31,000	22,000
	118,000	99,000

Complete the following table to show the performance indicators listed for each year. Show the solutions to two decimal places, with the exception of those measured in days which should be rounded to the nearest day.

	20-8	20-7
Gross Profit %		
Return on Capital Employed %		
Operating Profit as % Sales		
Asset Turnover		
Trade Receivables Days		
Trade Payables Days		

7.2   The performance indicators shown in the following table have been calculated for a trading company. Match the comments on performance shown with the appropriate measure of performance.

Performance Indicator	20-8	20-7	Comments
Gross Profit %	24.88	22.96	The profit before interest as a percentage of sales has increased in the later year
Return on Capital Employed %	18.35	17.99	There is less value of sales compared to total resources in the later year
Operating Profit as % Sales	13.88	12.76	The profit as a percentage of sales (after taking into account just the cost of sales) has improved from the first year to the second
Asset Turnover	1.32	1.41	Credit customers are taking slightly longer on average to pay in the later year than they were in the previous year
Trade Receivables Days	70	67	The operating profit as a percentage of total resources has increased from year to year
Trade Payables Days	107	109	The company is paying its credit suppliers in a similar timescale in both years

7.3   Utoxx Limited has developed a potion which claims to detoxify individuals. The product competes with those from several other companies. Meetox is a major competitor and market leader, with over half of the market. You have been given the following information about Utoxx and Meetox for the year just ended.

Statement of profit or loss	Utoxx	Meetox
	£000	£000
Sales revenue	12,000	50,000
Cost of production		
Direct (raw) materials	2,800	8,600
Direct labour	1,900	4,200
Fixed production overheads	1,500	9,000
Total cost of sales	6,200	21,800
Gross profit	**5,800**	**28,200**
Selling and distribution costs	1,200	2,000
Administration costs	950	2,500
Advertising costs	900	18,000
Operating profit	2,750	5,700

Other information		Utoxx	Meetox
Number of units sold	**Units**	1,200,000	4,500,000
Capital employed	(£000)	10,000	18,000

Calculate the performance indicators to complete the following table for Utoxx and Meetox:

Give answers to two decimal places.

	Utoxx	Meetox
Selling price per unit		
Material cost per unit		
Labour cost per unit		
Fixed production overheads per unit		
Gross profit margin		
Operating profit margin		
Advertising cost as % of turnover		
Return on capital employed		

7.4 The table below shows the current situation for a company that buys and sells a single product. Current sales are 2,500 units per month, based on a selling price of £15.

Inventory is valued at variable cost and is equal to 3 months' sales. Customers take 2.5 months to pay. Payables relate to variable costs and are paid in 2 months.

A suggestion has been made to reduce the selling price by 20% to £12, which it is thought will result in an increased sales volume of 40%.

Complete the table based on the proposal, assuming that net current asset periods remain the same.

	Current Position	**Proposed Position**
Monthly Statement of Profit or Loss	£	£
Sales	37,500	
Variable Costs	25,000	
Fixed Costs	5,000	
Operating Profit	7,500	
Net Current Assets		
Inventory	75,000	
Receivables	93,750	
Less Payables	(50,000)	
Total Net Current Assets (exc cash)	118,750	

7.5   Analyse each of the following cost examples into the four main groups of the cost of quality by ticking the appropriate columns.

	Prevention Costs	Appraisal Costs	Internal Failure Costs	External Failure Costs
Production staff training costs				
Costs of customer complaints section				
Costs of re-inspection of reworked products				
Inspection of work in progress				
Testing of finished goods				
Loss of customer goodwill				
Customer compensation payments				

7.6　The four perspectives used by the balanced scorecard are:

- Financial
- Customer
- Internal
- Innovation and Learning

The following table shows what each perspective is concerned with and ratios that can be used to measure aspects of that perspective.

Complete the table by inserting the correct perspective in each row.

Perspective	What it is concerned with	Typical ratios that can be used
	Technical excellence and quality issues	Added Value, Cost of Quality, Reject Rates, Sales returns (due to quality issues) as a % of net sales.
	Customer satisfaction and loyalty	Delivery times (or order backlogs), Repeat orders from customers, Sales returns as a % of net sales.
	Improvement of existing products or services, and development of new products or services	R & D Expenditure (or as %), Revenue from new products (or as %).
	Satisfying the shareholders, primarily by generating profits	Gross Profit %, Operating Profit %, ROCE, Added Value.

7.7　A company has three divisions, Aye, Bee, and Cee. Details of the divisional operating profits and investments are shown in the following table.

The company cost of capital is 15%.

Complete the table to show the return on investment (to two decimal places), and the residual income of each division.

	Division Aye	Division Bee	Division Cee
Operating profit £	1,250,000	436,000	1,950,000
Investment £million	6.1	2.3	6.5
Return on investment %			
Residual income £			

8 Statistical techniques

8.1 Sales (in units) of a product are changing at a broadly steady rate and don't seem to be affected by any seasonal variations. Use the average change in the data given for the first five periods to forecast the sales for periods 6 and 7.

Period	1	2	3	4	5	6	7
Sales (units)	89,500	90,150	90,700	91,300	91,900	92550	93100

650   550   600   600

8.2 Computer modelling has been used to identify the regression formula for the monthly total of a specific indirect cost as:

Y = £19.30 x + £595.00

Where y is total monthly cost

And x is monthly production in units

Calculate the total monthly cost when output is

• 900 units, and

• 1,500 units

8.3   A company has sales data that follows a 3 period cycle. The sales units shown in the table below have been compiled from actual data in periods 30 to 36.

Period	Actual data/ Forecast data	3 point moving averages (Trend)	Seasonal variations
30	1,550		
31	1,440	1460	-20
32	1,390	1420	-30
33	1,430	1380	50
34	1,320	1340	-20
35	1,270	1300	-30
36	1,310	1260	50
37			-20
38			-30
39			50
40			-20

Complete the table to show your responses to the following:

(a)   Using a 3 point moving average, calculate the trend figures and the seasonal variations for periods 31 to 35.

(b)   Extrapolate the trend to periods 37 to 40, and using the seasonal variations forecast the sales units for those periods.

8.4   This year's sales are £1,500,000. Analysis of recent years shows: /4 = 375,000

- a growth trend of 3% per annum

- seasonal variations from the trend of:

    Quarter 1   −£50,000

    Quarter 2   +£10,000

    Quarter 3   +£75,000

    Quarter 4   −£35,000

Forecast the sales for each quarter of next year, using the following table.

	£
Quarter 1	336,250
Quarter 2	396,250
Quarter 3	461,250
Quarter 4	351,250
Total Sales	1,545,000

8.5   The trend in the number of units sold per quarter was 7,400 in the last quarter of the current year. The trend increases by 50 units per quarter.

The seasonal variations are a percentage of the trend for the quarter, and have been established as:

    Quarter 1   −10%
    Quarter 2   −15%
    Quarter 3   +35%
    Quarter 4   −10%

The selling price for each unit will be £22 in the next year. Complete the following table to establish the data for the sales budget for next year. Calculate the unit forecast to the nearest whole unit.

	Trend (units)	**Forecast** (units)	**Forecast sales £**
Quarter 1			
Quarter 2			
Quarter 3			
Quarter 4			
Total			

8.6 The table below contains the last three months' cost per kilogram for product Alpha.

January	February	March
Actual price was £20.40	Actual price was £19.20	Actual price was £21.00
Seasonal variation was +£1.20	Seasonal variation was −£0.30	Seasonal variation was +£1.20

19.2   *19.50*   *19.8*

The trend in prices is an increase of £ ⬚ *0.30* per month.

8.7 A company has provided the following information:

	January	February	March
Total cost	£150,000	£168,000	£225,000
Total quantity purchased	10,000 kg	10,500 kg	12,500 kg

15   *18*

The cost index for March based upon January being the base period of 100 is:

18/15 = 1.2
×100

(a)	150	
(b)	125	
(c)	120	✓
(d)	83	

8.8 The cost per unit of a product has increased from £50 in January to £54 in April. The cost per unit was £40 when the index was rebased to 100.

(a)	The cost index in April was 135 and the increase from January to April is 8.0%	✓
(b)	The cost index in April was 108 and the increase from January to April is 8.0%	
(c)	The cost index in April is 125 and the increase from January to April is 35.0%	
(d)	The cost index in April is 135 and the increase from January to April is 4.0%	

8.9   The table below shows details of five unrelated materials. Complete the blank parts of the table. Show all figures to two decimal places.

Material	Old price £	New price £	New price as index number with old price as base	% increase in price
A	13.56	14.16		
B	10.60	11.00		
C	13.00	13.75		
D	21.50		105.00	
E	48.00		124.00	

8.10   A company is considering launching one of two new products, and it has carried out market research on them both. This research has been combined with accounting data to provide the following profit outcomes for each product. The following table shows this data.

Product A			Product B		
Probability	Profit £'000	Weighted Profit £'000	Probability	Profit £'000	Weighted Profit £'000
0.1	300		0.1	270	
0.2	420		0.4	500	
0.5	550		0.3	550	
0.1	620		0.1	600	
0.1	800		0.1	650	
Expected value			Expected value		

- Complete the table to calculate the expected value of the profit for each product

- Analyse and comment on the likely profitability of the two products. Make a recommendation as to which product you consider to be the best alternative.

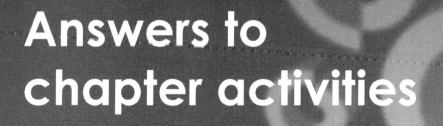

Answers to
chapter activities

1 Preparing budgets

1.1 (b), (c), (e) and (f)

1.2

	Cost of production	Maintenance	Capital expenditure	Marketing	Finance
Direct labour wages	✔				
Interest charges					✔
New computer system			✔		
Entertaining customers				✔	
Hire of machinery testing equipment		✔			
Raw materials usage	✔				

1.3

Number of Units	Week 1	Week 2	Week 3	Week 4	Week 5
Opening inventory	4,000	5,000	4,400	4,200	4,800
Production	11,000	11,900	10,800	11,100	11,200
Sub-total	15,000	16,900	15,200	15,300	16,000
Forecast sales	10,000	12,500	11,000	10,500	12,000
Closing inventory	5,000	4,400	4,200	4,800	4,000

1.4 The number of overtime hours required to be worked in October is **160 hours**

1.5

Product	Units	Hours per unit	Hours required
Alpha	190	1.0	190
Beta	200	2.5	500
Gamma	270	3.2	864
Total machine hours for department K			1,554

2 additional machines should be hired.

1.6 **(a)**

Raw materials	kg	£
Opening inventory of raw materials	3,500	7,000
Purchases of raw materials	32,000	64,000
Sub-total	35,500	71,000
Used in production	30,000	60,000
Closing inventory of raw materials	5,500	11,000

(b)

Direct labour	Hours	Cost £
Basic time at £10 per hour	3,520	35,200
Overtime	480	7,200
Total	4,000	42,400

(c)

Overheads	Hours	Cost £
Variable overheads at £2.00 per hour	4,000	8,000
Fixed overheads		12,000
Total overheads		20,000

(d)

Operating budget	Units	per unit £	£
Sales	38,000	4.50	171,000
Cost of goods sold:			
Opening inventory of finished goods			15,300
Cost of production:		£	
Raw materials		60,000	
Direct labour		42,400	
Production overheads		20,000	
Total cost of production			122,400
Closing inventory of finished goods			21,420
Cost of goods sold			116,280
Gross profit			54,720
Non-production overheads		£	
Administration		15,000	
Marketing		12,500	
Total non-production overheads			27,500
Net profit			27,220

1.7

Cash forecast – August	£
Opening cash balance	16,400
Receipts from sales	8,540
Payments for:	
Purchases	5,100
Wages	2,300
Expenses	880
Capital expenditure	4,500
Total payments	12,780
Closing cash balance	12,160

2   Using budgets

2.1

	Budget for the year	Budget for April
Units sold	36,000	3,000
Units produced	40,000	3,500
	£	£
Sales	540,000	45,000
Cost of production:		
Materials used	108,000	9,450
Labour	122,400	10,950
Variable production overhead	20,000	1,750
Fixed production overhead	18,000	1,500

2.2

	Budget for the year	Budget for week 14
Units sold	850,000	16,800
Units produced	860,000	17,000
	£	£
Sales	8,075,000	159,600
Costs of production:		
Materials used	1,754,400	34,680
Labour	2,720,000	53,000
Variable production overhead	1,978,000	39,100
Fixed production overhead	1,040,000	20,000
Total cost of production	7,492,400	146,780

2.3   70,000 / 13,000 = between 5 and 6, so 6 machines will be needed at that level of production. Six machines will be able to cope with between 65,001 and 78,000 units.

Budgeted machine hire cost will be £45,000 / 6 = £7,500 per machine.

(a)   60,000 units requires 5 machines, costing £37,500

(b)   68,000 units requires 6 machines, costing £45,000

(c)   80,000 units requires 7 machines, costing £52,500

2.4

Operating budget	First scenario	Alternative scenario
Selling price per unit	£11.50	£11.73
Sales volume	190,000	180,500
	£	£
Sales revenue	2,185,000	2,117,265
Costs:		
Materials	541,500	514,425
Labour	570,000	541,500
Depreciation	182,000	182,000
Energy	124,000	122,366
Occupancy costs	203,600	208,690
Total costs	1,621,100	1,568,981
Operating profit	563,900	548,284
Increase / (decrease) in profit		(15,616)

2.5

	Original budget	Actual	Flexed budget	Variances Fav / (Adv)
Volume (units)	50,000	60,000	60,000	
	£	£	£	£
Sales revenue	2,250,000	2,640,000	2,700,000	(60,000)
Costs:				
Materials	600,000	780,000	720,000	(60,000)
Labour	750,000	895,000	900,000	5,000
Distribution	200,000	255,000	240,000	(15,000)
Energy	79,000	85,000	94,000	9,000
Equipment hire	15,000	22,000	18,000	(4,000)
Depreciation	24,000	24,000	24,000	0
Marketing	28,000	30,000	28,000	(2,000)
Administration	45,000	44,500	45,000	500
Total Costs	1,741,000	2,135,500	2,069,000	(66,500)
Operating profit	509,000	504,500	631,000	(126,500)

2.6   The following statements are consistent with the operating statement and information provided and could form part of a report.

(b), (e), (f), (i), (k) and (l)

2.7

	Budget 1	Budget 2	Actual	Flexed budget	Variances Fav / (Adv)
Units	10,000	15,000	11,500	11,500	
	£	£	£	£	£
Sales	900,000	1,350,000	1,058,000	1,035,000	23,000
Materials	250,000	375,000	299,000	287,500	(11,500)
Labour	350,000	500,000	380,000	395,000	15,000
Production overheads	170,000	195,000	190,000	177,500	(12,500)
Administration overheads	60,000	60,000	62,000	60,000	(2,000)
Operating profit	70,000	220,000	127,000	115,000	12,000

Flexed Budget Workings:

Sales — Selling price is £90 per unit x 11,500 units = £1,035,000

Materials — Variable cost of £25 per unit x 11,500 units = £287,500

Labour — Semi-variable cost: use high-low method

Variable (£500,000 – £350,000) / (15,000 – 10,000 units) = £30 per unit

Fixed = £350,000 – (£30 x 10,000) = £50,000

Production Overheads — Semi-variable cost: use high-low method

Variable (£195,000 – £170,000) / (15,000 – 10,000 units) = £5 per unit

Fixed = £170,000 – (£5 x 10,000) = £120,000

3 Standard costing – direct costs

3.1 (d) £600 Favourable

3.2 (b) £1,300 Adverse

3.3 (a) £87,500

3.4

Variance	£	A / F
Direct material (paint) price variance	130	F
Direct material (sheet steel) usage variance	750	A
Direct labour rate variance	2,050	A
Direct labour efficiency variance	6,000	F

Variance Workings:

Paint price:	(650 litres x £5) – £3,120	= £130 F
Steel usage:	((11,500 x 3) – 35,000) x £1.50	= £750 A
Labour rate:	(4,100 x £12) – £51,250	= £2,050 A
Labour efficiency:	((11,500 x 0.4) – 4,100) x £12	= £6,000 F

3.5

Budgeted / Standard cost of materials for actual production			£97,500
Variances:	**Favourable £**	**Adverse £**	
Direct material price	1,560		
Direct material usage		3,900	
Total variance		2,340	+£2,340
Actual cost of materials for actual production			£99,840

3.6

Budgeted / Standard cost of labour for actual production			£3,750.00
Variances:	Favourable £	Adverse £	
Direct labour rate		107.50	
Direct labour efficiency		87.50	
Total variance		195.00	+£195.00
Actual cost of labour for actual production			£3,945.00

Standard costing – overheads and sales

4.1

1 unit of Zed	Quantity	Cost per unit £	Total cost £
Material	12 kg	8.50	102.00
Labour	0.6 hour	15.00	9.00
Fixed costs	1 unit	80.00	80.00
Total			191.00

4.2   The fixed overhead volume variance is **£100,000 adverse**.

The fixed overhead expenditure variance is **£20,000 favourable.**

4.3   The fixed overhead volume variance is **£16,000 adverse**.

The fixed overhead expenditure variance is **£5,000 adverse.**

4.4

	Variance £	A / F
Expenditure Variance	2,000	F
Volume Variance	6,000	A
Total Fixed Overhead Variances	4,000	A

4.5   **(a)** is false; **(b)** is true

4.6

Budgeted / Standard fixed cost for actual production			£437,500
Variances:	**Favourable £**	**Adverse £**	
Fixed overhead expenditure	10,500		
Fixed overhead volume	7,500		
Total variance	18,000		–£18,000
Actual fixed cost for actual production			£419,500

4.7   **(a)**   Variable overhead price (or expenditure) variance:

(5,400 direct labour hours x £3.50) – £19,100

= £200 Adverse

(b)   Variable overhead efficiency variance:

(0.5 hours x 10,500 units x £3.50) – (5,400 hours x £3.50)

= £18,375 – £18,900

= £525 Adverse

4.8   **(a)**   Variable overhead price (or expenditure) variance:

(1,990 machine hours £13*) – £27,600

= £1,730 Adverse

*Standard hourly rate = £1.30 x 10

(b)   Variable overhead efficiency variance:

(0.1 hours x 20,250 units x £13) – (1,990 hours x £13)

= £26,325 – £25,870

= £455 Favourable

4.9

Email

To: Production Director

From: Accounting Technician

Date: xx

Subject: Reasons for Variances

The following sets out some possible reasons for the adverse variances that occurred based on the September operations.

The direct material price variance relates to the buying price of raw potatoes. The recent UK weather created a poor potato harvest, and the subsequent shortage of potatoes led to a price increase. This price increase would have been across the whole UK market.

The direct material usage variance relates to the additional cost incurred due to using more raw potatoes than expected to make the average bag of frozen chips. This appears to be due to the poor quality of potatoes, which meant that more partly processed output had to be rejected.

The adverse direct labour rate variance may be caused by the use of overtime rates to pay for the additional time required by the quality control operatives. The overtime rate was paid to satisfy the need to spend more time discarding the blemished chips that occurred due to the quality of the potatoes.

The direct labour efficiency variance is also related to the work of the labour-intensive quality control function. Since there were so many blemished chips to be removed, the conveyor had to be slowed down, and this increased the labour time needed to check the output.

The fixed overhead expenditure variance relates to the additional fixed overheads incurred in September. One such cost was incurred when the conveyor broke down and a contractor was utilised to supply and fit replacement parts.

The fixed overhead volume variance is caused by spreading the fixed overheads over a smaller amount of output than was budgeted. It seems likely that in September the output was lower than budgeted due to the greater proportion of the input that was rejected in the form of blemished chips, together with the linked issue of the slow running of the conveyor.

Overall the adverse variances mean that the actual cost of the September production was £30,000 more than the standard cost of the same production level.

4.10

Standard unit profit	£450 – (£180 + £230)	= £40
Sales price variance	£2,640,000 – (£450 x 6,000 units)	= £60,000 A
Sales volume variance	(6,000 units x £40) – (5,800 units x £40)	= £8,000 F
Total sales variance	£60,000 A – £8,000 F	= £52,000 A

5 | Cost management techniques

5.1 • **Current absorption rate per hour for production overheads**

Annual production overheads		£6,885,000

Annual hours calculation

Rapier motorcycles	6 batches x 500 units x 50 hours	= 150,000 hours
Custom motorcycles	6 batches x 10 units x 50 hours	= 3,000 hours
Total hours		= 153,000 hours

Absorption rate per hour	£6,885,000 / 153,000 hours	= £45 per hour

• **Absorption rate excluding set-up costs**

Annual production overheads	£6,885,000
Set-up costs	£ 306,000
Costs excluding set-ups	£6,579,000

Absorption rate per hour	£6,579,000 / 153,000 hours	= £43 per hour

• **Cost per set-up as a cost driver**

Annual costs of set-ups	£306,000
Number of set-ups per year	12
Cost per set-up	£25,500

• **Cost of set-ups per unit of each motorcycle**

Rapier	£25,500 / 500 units (batch)	= £51 per unit
Custom	£25,500 / 10 units (batch)	= £2,550 per unit

- **Revised costs per unit of each motorcycle**

	Rapier	Custom
	£	£
Materials and Components	3,700	5,400
Direct Labour	1,000	1,400
Cost of set-ups	51	2,550
Other production overheads (50 x £43)	2,150	2,150
Total cost	6,901	11,500

5.2   **(a)** and **(c)** are Activity based costing; **(b)** and **(e)** are Marginal costing; **(d)** is Absorption costing

5.3

Maximum production cost per unit	£5.25
Build-up of maximum production cost per unit:	
Materials	£1.85 (balancing figure)
Labour	£1.40
Overheads	£2.00
Maximum cost per kilo for material T	£3.70

5.4

Year	Cash Inflow £000	Cash Outflow £000	Net Cash Flow £000	Discount Factor	Present Value £000
0	0	4,800	−4,800	1.000	−4,800
1	0	4,800	−4,800	0.909	−4,363
2	0	12,300	−12,300	0.826	−10,160
3	32,000	15,000	17,000	0.751	12,767
4	32,000	15,000	17,000	0.683	11,611
5	24,000	10,000	14,000	0.621	8,694
	Totals		26,100		13,749

5.5 **(a)**

	£
Sales price per unit	40.00
Profit margin	18.00
Total costs	22.00
Fixed cost per unit	12.00
Labour cost per unit	6.00
Maximum material cost per unit	4.00
Target cost per kilogram	20.00

(b) The trade price quoted on the supplier's price list is £25 per kilogram. The Purchasing Manager has negotiated a discount of 15%. The discount should be **rejected** because the £25 reduces to **£21.25** which is **above** the Target cost.

(c) The minimum percentage discount needed to achieve the Target cost is **20%**

6 Decision making techniques

6.1

	Baked Beans	Garden Peas	Total
Volume (units)	2,500,000	1,000,000	
	£000	£000	£000
Sales	500	220	720
Variable costs of production / purchase	150	140	290
Direct fixed costs of production	80	0	80
Previously shared fixed costs of production	150	0	150
Gross profit	120	80	200
Administration costs			40
Selling and distribution costs			35
Operating profit			125

6.2

	Units	Price/cost £	Total £
Additional revenue	2,000,000	0.50	1,000,000
Savings on materials	2,000,000	0.30	600,000
Reduction in selling and distribution costs			100,000
Additional depreciation			(800,000)
Additional annual profit			900,000

6.3

	Total per Week £
Incremental revenue	120,000
Incremental costs:	
Variable production costs	33,000
Purchase of finished goods	81,000
Fixed production costs	0
Incremental profit / (loss)	6,000

	Accept	Reject
Recommendation	✓	

Workings:

Incremental revenue	7,500 x £16	= £120,000
Variable production costs	3,000 x £11	= £33,000
Purchase of finished goods	4,500 x £18	= £81,000

6.4   (a)   Calculation of usage of material in original budget:

Xenox	£90,000 / £0.60 = 150,000 kilos	(= 5 kilos per unit)
Zenley	£120,000 / £0.60 = 200,000 kilos	(= 4 kilos per unit)

Contribution per kilo of material:

Xenox	£150,000 / 150,000 kilos	= £1.00 per kilo
Zenley	£430,000 / 200,000 kilos	= £2.15 per kilo

Manufacture and sales should therefore be concentrated first on Zenley, followed by Xenox to use remaining material, as follows.

	Production volume	Material used (kilos)
Zenley	50,000	200,000
Xenox	10,000	50,000
		250,000

(b)

Revised Operating Budget July		Product Xenox		Product Zenley		Total
Manufacture & sales volume		10,000		50,000		60,000
			£		£	£
Sales revenue			120,000		900,000	1,020,000
Variable costs:						
Materials			30,000		120,000	150,000
Labour			40,000		350,000	390,000
Contribution			50,000		430,000	480,000
Fixed costs						450,000
Operating profit						30,000

6.5

	Eff	Gee
Contribution per kg material	£25	£20
Contribution per labour hour	£25	£30

Let F be number of Effs, and G be number of Gees.

Then, using material constraint:	2F + 1.5G	= 8,000	
And using labour constraint:	2F + G	= 6,500	
Subtracting gives	0.5G	= 1,500	so, G = 3,000
Using this in labour equation:	2F + 3,000	= 6,500	so, F = 1,750

	Eff	Gee	Total
Production (units)	1,750	3,000	4,750
Materials required (kg)	3,500	4,500	8,000
Labour required (hours)	3,500	3,000	6,500
Contribution	£87,500	£90,000	£177,500
Production (Eff units only)	3,250		
Comparative contribution	£162,500		
Production (Gee units only)		5,333	
Comparative contribution		£159,990	

Working for comparative figures:

If only Effs were produced, the material constraint would limit production to 8,000 / 2 = 4,000 units. The labour constraint would limit production to 6,500 / 2 = 3,250 units. The binding constraint would therefore be labour and only 3,250 units could be made.

If only Gees were produced, the material constraint would limit production to 8,000 / 1.5 = 5,333 units. The labour constraint would limit production to 6,500 / 1 = 6,500 units. The binding constraint would therefore be material and only 5,333 units could be made.

6.6

Year	Cash Outflow £	Cash Savings £	Discount Factor	Present Value £
0	600,000		1.000	(600,000)
1		140,000	0.952	133,280
2		140,000	0.907	126,980
3		140,000	0.864	120,960
4		140,000	0.823	115,220
5		140,000	0.784	109,760
Net Present Value				6,200

Cash savings:

Labour savings	£160,000
Less increased production costs	£ 20,000
	———
	£140,000

6.7

Year	Cash Flow	Disc Factor 10%	Disc Cash Flow 10%	Disc Factor 15%	Disc Cash Flow 15%
0	−3,000,000	1.000	−3,000,000	1.000	−3,000,000
1	780,000	0.909	709,020	0.870	678,600
2	780,000	0.826	644,280	0.756	589,680
3	780,000	0.751	585,780	0.658	513,240
4	780,000	0.683	532,740	0.572	446,160
5	780,000	0.621	484,380	0.497	387,660
6	780,000	0.564	439,920	0.432	336,960
Net Present Values			396,120		−47,700

The net present value of the project using a discount factor of 10% is + £396,120

The payback period in years is 4 years to the nearest year

The discounted payback period is 5 years to the nearest year

The estimated internal rate of return to one decimal place

10% + ((396,120 / 443,820) x 5%) = 14.5%

The accounting rate of return to the nearest whole %

(280,000 / 1,500,000) x 100%   =19%

7   Performance indicators

7.1

	20-8	20-7
Gross Profit %	24.88	22.96
Return on Capital Employed %	18.35	17.99
Operating Profit as % Sales	13.88	12.76
Asset Turnover	1.32	1.41
Trade Receivables Days	70	67
Trade Payables Days	107	109

Note that when calculating the gearing ratio, preference shares are treated in a similar way to long term debt.

7.2

Performance Indicator	20-8	20-7	Comments
Gross Profit %	24.88	22.96	The profit as a percentage of sales (after taking into account just the cost of sales) has improved from the first year to the second
Return on Capital Employed %	18.35	17.99	The operating profit as a percentage of total resources has increased from year to year
Operating Profit as % Sales	13.88	12.76	The profit before interest as a percentage of sales has increased in the later year
Asset Turnover	1.32	1.41	There is less value of sales compared to total resources in the later year
Trade Receivables Days	70	67	Credit customers are taking slightly longer on average to pay in the later year than they were in the previous year
Trade Payables Days	107	109	The company is paying its credit suppliers in a similar timescale in both years

7.3

	Utoxx	Meetox
Selling price per unit	£10.00	£11.11
Material cost per unit	£2.33	£1.91
Labour cost per unit	£1.58	£0.93
Fixed production overheads per unit	£1.25	£2.00
Gross profit margin	48.33%	56.40%
Operating profit margin	22.92%	11.40%
Advertising cost as % of turnover	7.50%	36.00%
Return on capital employed	27.50%	31.67%

7.4

	Current Position	Proposed Position
Monthly Statement of Profit or Loss	£	£
Sales	37,500	42,000
Variable Costs	25,000	35,000
Fixed Costs	5,000	5,000
Operating Profit	7,500	2,000
Net Current Assets		
Inventory	75,000	105,000
Receivables	93,750	105,000
Less Payables	(50,000)	(70,000)
Total Net Current Assets (exc cash)	118,750	140,000

7.5

	Prevention Costs	Appraisal Costs	Internal Failure Costs	External Failure Costs
Production staff training costs	✓			
Costs of customer complaints section				✓
Costs of re-inspection of reworked products			✓	
Inspection of work in progress		✓		
Testing of finished goods		✓		
Loss of customer goodwill				✓
Customer compensation payments				✓

7.6

Perspective	What it is concerned with	Typical ratios that can be used
Internal	Technical excellence and quality issues	Added Value, Cost of Quality, Reject Rates, Sales returns (due to quality issues) as a % of net sales.
Customer	Customer satisfaction and loyalty	Delivery times (or order backlogs), Repeat orders from customers, Sales returns as a % of net sales.
Innovation and Learning	Improvement of existing products or services, and development of new products or services	R & D Expenditure (or as %), Revenue from new products (or as %).
Financial	Satisfying the shareholders, primarily by generating profits	Gross Profit %, Operating Profit %, ROCE, Added Value.

7.7

	Division Aye	Division Bee	Division Cee
Operating profit £	1,250,000	436,000	1,950,000
Investment £million	6.1	2.3	6.5
Return on investment %	20.49	18.96	30.00
Residual income £	335,000	91,000	975,000

8 Statistical techniques

8.1

Period	1	2	3	4	5	6	7
Sales (units)	89,500	90,150	90,700	91,300	91,900	92,500	93,100

8.2   Output 900 units:

Cost =   (£19.30 x 900) + £595.00   = £17,965.00

Output 1,500 units:

Cost =   (£19.30 x 1,500) + £595.00   = £29,545.00

8.3   **(a) and (b)**

Period	Actual data/ Forecast data	3 point moving averages (Trend)	Seasonal variations
30	1,550		
31	1,440	1,460	−20
32	1,390	1,420	−30
33	1,430	1,380	+50
34	1,320	1,340	−20
35	1,270	1,300	−30
36	1,310		
37	1,200	1,220	−20
38	1,150	1,180	−30
39	1,190	1,140	+50
40	1,080	1,100	−20

8.4

	£
Quarter 1	336,250
Quarter 2	396,250
Quarter 3	461,250
Quarter 4	351,250
Total Sales	1,545,000

8.5

	Trend (units)	**Forecast** (units)	**Forecast sales £**
Quarter 1	7,450	6,705	147,510
Quarter 2	7,500	6,375	140,250
Quarter 3	7,550	10,193	224,246
Quarter 4	7,600	6,840	150,480
Total		30,113	662,486

8.6   The trend in prices is an increase of **£0.30** per month.

8.7   (c)   120 (Cost per kilo £18.00 compared with £15.00)

8.8   (a)   The cost index in April was 135 and the increase from January to April is 8.0%

8.9

Material	Old price £	New price £	New price as index number with old price as base	% increase in price
A	13.56	14.16	104.42	4.42
B	10.60	11.00	103.77	3.77
C	13.00	13.75	105.77	5.77
D	21.50	22.58	105.00	5.00
E	48.00	59.52	124.00	24.00

8.10

Product A			Product B		
Probability	**Profit £'000**	**Weighted Profit £'000**	**Probability**	**Profit £'000**	**Weighted Profit £'000**
0.1	300	30	0.1	270	27
0.2	420	84	0.4	500	200
0.5	550	275	0.3	550	165
0.1	620	62	0.1	600	60
0.1	800	80	0.1	650	65
	Expected value	531		Expected value	517

Product A has a higher expected value than product B, although the figures are quite similar. Both the lowest profit outcome and the highest profit outcome are greater for product A than product B.

The most likely outcome for product A is a profit of £550,000, and there is a 50% chance of this occurring. The most likely outcome for product B is a lower profit of £500,000, and this has a 40% chance of occurring.

Product A has an 80% chance of generating a profit of £550,000 or more, with a maximum possible profit of £800,000. Product B has only a 50% chance of a profit of £550,000 or more, and a lower maximum profit of £650,000

Overall product A is the better alternative, based on the data provided.

Practice
assessment 1

Task 1

(a) Select the appropriate term from the options given to match the description.

Description	Term	
Budgets that are continually extended into the future as time moves forward	Incremental budgets	
	Flexible budgets	
	Rolling budgets	✓
	Activity based budgets	

(b) Who would you contact in each of the following situations?

(a)	You want to know details of planned pay rises	5
(b)	You want details of the sales forecast	4
(c)	You want details of planned acquisitions of non-current assets	1

Select from:

1   Capital expenditure budget working group

2   Production Director

3   Purchasing Manager

4   Sales Director

5   Human Resources Manager

6   Marketing Manager

(c) Complete the following table by using ticks to show into which budget(s) each item of cost would occur.

	Direct cost of production	Production overheads	Capital expenditure	Marketing	Cash
Extension to offices			✓		✓
Depreciation of production equipment		✓			
Indirect production labour	✗	✓			✓
Advertising campaign costs				✓	✓
Hire of production equipment	✗	✓			✓
Printing customer perceptions questionnaire				✓	✓

(d) Select an appropriate accounting treatment for each of the following costs from the options available.

(a)	Employers' National Insurance for administration staff	4 2
(b)	Material usage for production	3
(c)	Rent of photocopier	2
(d)	Cost of the stores department	6 1
(e)	Cost of idle time for production operatives	6
(f)	Cost of productive time for production operatives	3

Options available are:

1   Activity based charge to production cost centres

2   Allocate to administration overheads

3   Direct cost

4   Allocate to finance overheads

5   Allocate to selling and distribution overheads

6   Allocate to production overheads

Task 2

(a) The number of units of a product that are required are shown below. 7% of the units produced fail a quality control test and are scrapped. Complete the table to show the number of units that must be manufactured to allow for this rejection rate.

	Month 1	Month 2	Month 3
Required units	75,330	79,980	77,190
Manufactured units	81000	86000	83000

(b) 50,000 units of finished product are to be manufactured during October. Each unit takes three minutes to produce. 12 staff each work 180 basic hours in October.

Complete the following sentences: $12 \times 180 = 2160$ hrs ava

$50,000 \times 3/60 = 2500$

The number of units that can be made in basic time during October is $\boxed{43200}$

$2160 \times 60/3 = 43200$

The number of overtime hours required to be worked in October is $\boxed{340}$

$2500 - 2160 = 340$

(c) A company has budgeted to make and sell 60,000 units in the coming year.

Each unit takes 20 minutes to make and requires 2.5 kg of raw material. The quality control department can test 4,200 units each month. A contract has been placed to purchase 100,000 kg of raw material at an agreed price. Further supplies can be obtained on the open market but the price is likely to be much higher. The company employs 10 production workers. Each worker works 1,750 hours a year in normal time. $10 \times 1750 = 17500$ hrs

$17500 \times 60/20 = 52500$

Complete the following analysis. 52500

There is labour available to make $\boxed{52500}$ units in normal time. Therefore, $\boxed{7500}$ hours of overtime will be needed.

The raw material contract will provide enough material to make $\boxed{40000}$ units.

Therefore, $\boxed{50,000}$ kg will have to be purchased on the open market.

Quality control can test $\boxed{50400}$ units in the year. It will be necessary to make alternative arrangements for $\boxed{9600}$ units.

(d)   A company has already produced budgets based on its first scenario.

Assumptions in the first scenario:

- Materials and labour are variable costs
- Depreciation is a stepped fixed cost increasing every 25,000 units
- Energy costs are semi-variable, with a fixed element of £37,000
- Occupancy costs behave as fixed costs

The alternative scenario is based on:

- A decrease in selling price of 2%
- An increase in sales volume of 8%
- An increase in only the variable cost of energy of 2%
- An increase in occupancy costs of 4.5%

Apart from the selling price per unit, do not enter any decimals. Round to the nearest whole number if necessary.

Operating budget	First scenario	Alternative scenario
Selling price per unit	£15.00	14.70
Sales volume	130,000	140,400
	£	£
Sales revenue	1,950,000	2,063,880
Costs:		
Materials	585,000	631800
Labour	390,000	421200
Depreciation	180,000	180,000
Energy	115,000	122925
Occupancy costs	189,400	197923
Total costs	1,459,400	1553848
Operating profit	490,600	510,032
Increase / (decrease) in profit		19432

(i)   Complete the alternative scenario column in the operating budget table and calculate the increase or decrease in expected profit.

(ii) Consider the assumptions that have been used in part (i), and discuss whether the assumptions could be subject to any uncertainty.

Task 3

(a) Select the appropriate term from the options given to match the description.

Description	Term	
The difference between the expected and actual cost of direct materials that is due to using a different quantity of materials than standard	Direct material price variance	
	Direct material usage variance	✓
	Direct material cost variance	
	Direct material efficiency variance	

did

(b) The operating statement for June showed that the direct raw material costs were £26,895. 3,300 kilos of material were used and 5,500 items were produced. The standard cost allows 0.58 kilos of material for each item, at a standard price of £8.00 per kilo.   *8 x 0·58 x*
5500

Complete the following table, and show whether each variance is favourable or adverse.

Price *Actual* *Usage* *standard*

Direct raw material costs			Fav / Adv
Flexed budget (standard cost)	£ 25520		
Actual price per kilo (to £0.01)	£ 8·15		
Actual material used per item	0·6	kg	
Price variance	£ 495		Adv
Usage variance	£ 880 ?		Adv
Cost variance	£ 1375		Adv
Cost variance % (to 0.1%)	5·4	%	

1375 / 25520 x 100

(c) Prepare the direct labour cost statement from the activity data provided.

Round to the nearest whole number if necessary. Show adverse variances as negative amounts.

Activity data	Items produced	Labour hours	Cost £
Budget *7800*	19,500 *0·4hrs*	7,800	140,400 *17800 = £18*
Actual results *7000*	17,500 *0·4hrs*	7,000	122,500 *7000 = £17.50*

17500 x 0·4 x 18
= 126.000

0·5 x 7000 = 3500

Direct labour cost statement	£
Standard labour cost of production	126.000
Labour rate variance	3500
Labour efficiency variance	0
Labour cost variance	3500

standard
17500 x 18 x 0·4
= 126000·20

126000 - 122500 = 3500

Task 4

A company manufactures two products, Alpha and Delta. The two overhead activities, materials handling, and production set-up, have budgets of £3,500,000 and £2,000,000 respectively. ~~£5,500,000~~

Alpha uses two hours of direct labour per unit, and Delta uses one hour.

The following table provides additional information.

	Alpha	**Delta**
Direct materials per unit	£6.00	£10.00
Direct labour per unit *2 =*	£30.00 *1 =*	£15.00
Number of material requisitions *mat handling*	175	700
Number of production set-ups *prod set up*	50	200
Budgeted production units	87,500	100,000

(a)   Complete the following table, using Activity Based Costing principles.

Cost driver – per material requisition £	3,500,000 /875 = 4000	
Cost driver – per production set-up £	2,000,000 /250 = 8000	
	Alpha £	**Delta £**
Total materials handling cost	175 × 4000 = 700,000	700 × 4000 = 2,800,000
Total production set-up cost	50 × 8000 = 400,000	200 × 8000 = 1,600,000

(b)   Calculate total fixed overheads if they were absorbed on a budgeted labour hour basis, using the following:

Budgeted labour hours	275000	
Overhead absorption rate £	20	
	Alpha £	**Delta £**
Overheads per unit	2 × 20 = 40	1 × 20 = 20
Total overheads absorbed	3,500,000	2,000,000

5,500,000 /
275000
= 20

2 × 87500
= 175,000
× 100,000
275000
2

(c)   Explain which of the two methods of dealing with overheads produces the more useful management information.

(d)   Explain what cloud accounting is, and also discuss some of the advantages and disadvantages of businesses using it.

Task 5

A company manufactures two products, the Chef and the Field, both using the same material and the same grade of direct labour. The information below relates to the next reporting period.

Per Unit	Chef £	Field £
Direct materials at £6 per kg	12	18
Direct labour at £15 per hour	30	15
Variable overheads	4	2
Fixed production overheads	4	6
Selling price	70	65

The sales demand is for 10,000 Chefs and 15,000 Fields.   — 1·£0C

It is now established that materials will be limited to 50,000 kg and labour to 35,000 hours.

(a)   Complete the table below for the next period, calculating the optimal production.

	Chef	Field
Total direct materials required (kg)	20,000	45000 =65
Total direct labour required (hours)	20,000	15000 =35
Contribution per unit £	24	30
Contribution per limiting factor £ (to 2 d.p.)	12	10
Optimal production (units)	10000	10000

(b)   State the maximum additional amount that should be paid for each of the following resources if they were available:

	£
15,000 kg of additional material	150000
5,000 hours of additional labour	0

(c)   From the following statements regarding linear programming, select those that are true.

Statement	True ✔
Linear programming can only be used when there is a single constraint	
Linear programming assumes that the contribution per unit of each product remains constant, regardless of the volume produced	✓
Linear programming can usually be carried out using simultaneous equations or a graph	✓
Linear programming can be used where there are two products and two or more constraints	
Linear programming can only be used where there is a single product	
Linear programming assumes that the amount of resources required per unit of each product remains constant, regardless of the volume produced	✓
Linear programming ignores fixed costs	✓

Task 6

Delta Limited is considering investing in a project that will require an initial cash investment of £8,500,000 to purchase non-current assets. The assets will last five years, with no residual value. The annual profits are estimated at £800,000, after charging straight line depreciation for five years. All profits except depreciation are cash-based.

The company's cost of capital is 10%.

(a) Using the following table, calculate the net present value of the project.

Year	Cash Flow	Disc Factor 10%	Disc Cash Flow 10%
0	− 8,500,000	1.000	−8500,000
1		0.909	
2		0.826	
3		0.751	
4		0.683	
5		0.621	
Net Present Value			

(b) Calculate the payback period, to the nearest year

(c) Calculate the discounted payback period, to the nearest year

(d) The net present value of the project when using a discount factor of 15% is minus £117,500. Calculate the estimated internal rate of return to one decimal place

(e) Calculate the accounting rate of return to the nearest whole %, using the average investment

Task 7

Wye Limited is developing a new product and a colleague has prepared forecast information based upon two scenarios. The forecast income statement for both scenarios is shown below.

- Scenario 1 is to set the price at £15 per unit with sales of 80,000 units each year.

- Scenario 2 is to set the price at £13 per unit with sales of 120,000 units each year.

Forecast Income Statement	Scenario 1	Scenario 2
	£	£
Turnover	1,200,000	1,560,000
Cost of production		
Direct (Raw) Materials	240,000	360,000
Direct Labour	160,000	252,000
Fixed Production overheads	560,000	560,000
Total cost of sales	960,000	1,172,000
Gross profit	**240,000**	**388,000**
Selling and distribution costs	80,000	115,000
Administration costs	60,000	60,000
Operating profit	**100,000**	**213,000**

(a)   Calculate the following performance indicators for each scenario, using the following table. Round all answers to two decimal places.

	Scenario 1	Scenario 2
Gross Profit margin	20·/.	24·871
Operating profit margin	8·33·1.	13·65·.
Direct Materials as a percentage of turnover	20·/.	23·08·1.
Direct Materials cost per unit	£3	£3
Direct labour cost per unit	£2	£2·10
Fixed production cost per unit	£7	£4·67

(b)   Draft a report that analyses the performance under the two scenarios, referring to the performance indicators calculated in part (a). Recommend the course of action to take, including any provisos.

Task 8

(a)   A company has sales data that follows a 3 period cycle. The sales units shown in the table below have been compiled from actual data in periods 30 to 36.

Period	Actual data / Forecast data	3 point moving averages (Trend)	Seasonal variations
30	1,060		
31	1,095	1070	+25
32	1,055	1090	-35
33	1,120	1110	+10
34	1,155	1130	+25
35	1,115	1150	-35
36	1,180	1190	+10
37	1215	1190	+25
38	1175	1210	-35
39	1240	1230	+10
40	1275	1250	+25

Complete the table to show your responses to the following:

(1)   Using a 3 point moving average, calculate the trend figures and the seasonal variations for periods 31 to 35.

(2)   Extrapolate the trend to periods 37 to 40, and using the seasonal variations forecast the sales units for those periods.

(b)   Restate the following costs at January prices to the nearest £.

Month	Actual costs £	RPI	Costs at January prices £
January	115,600	246	115600
May	118,500	250	116604
October	119,000	252	116167

(c)   A business's total weekly production costs vary in line with the regression equation $y = a + bx$, where x is production volume. Total weekly production costs for 500 units are £11,000, and for 1,500 units are £21,000.

Calculate the values of 'a' and 'b' in the regression equation.

Practice assessment 2

Task 1

(a) Match the data in the first column with the appropriate source in the second column.

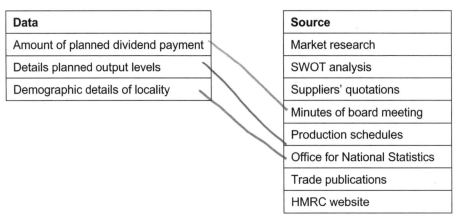

Data
Amount of planned dividend payment
Details planned output levels
Demographic details of locality

Source
Market research
SWOT analysis
Suppliers' quotations
Minutes of board meeting
Production schedules
Office for National Statistics
Trade publications
HMRC website

(b) Who would you contact in each of the following situations?

(a)	You want to know details of planned pay rises	5
(b)	You want details of planned production labour overtime	1
(c)	You want to know how many items are expected to be sold next month	4

Select from:

1 Production Planning Manager

2 Purchasing Manager

3 Budget Committee

4 Sales Director

5 Human Resources Manager

6 Marketing Manager

7 Training Manager

(c) For the following costs, select the most appropriate accounting treatment from the list below.

Costs:

(a)	Direct labour idle time	2
(b)	Raw materials usage	1
(c)	Interest on bank loan	6
(d)	Repairs to roof of factory and office building	3
(e)	Costs of running stores department	4
(f)	Interest charge for machinery acquired on finance lease	6
(g)	Direct labour productive time	1
(h)	Maintenance of factory machinery	2

Accounting treatments:

1   Direct production cost

2   Allocate to production overheads

3   Apportion to indirect costs of production and administration

4   Activity based charge to units of production

5   Allocate to indirect administration costs

6   Allocate to indirect finance costs

(d) Select the most appropriate term to match these descriptions from the list that follows:

Descriptions:

(a)	A cost that remains constant in total for a limited range of output volumes, and then moves to various higher amounts for higher volume levels	6
(b)	A collection of main budgets including budgeted statement of profit or loss and budgeted statement of financial position	9
(c)	A system where budgets are imposed on the organisation by senior managers	7
(d)	A type of sampling that can be used when a sampling frame cannot be established	11
(e)	A technique that can be used alongside budgeting where expected costs are calculated for each product and its components	3

List of Terms:

1	Participative budgeting	7	Top down budgeting
2	Variable cost	8	Fixed cost
3	Standard costing	9	Master budget
4	Cash budget	10	Bottom up budgeting
5	Random sampling	11	Quasi-random sampling
6	Stepped fixed cost		

(e) Select the appropriate term from the options given to match the description.

Descriptions	Term	
The manager responsible for a specific budget and the actual performance that is measured against that budget	Budget accountant	
	Budget holder	✓
	Budget committee	
	Budget manual	

Task 2

Operating Budget

Enter the missing figures in the working schedules and operating budget using the data from the production budget and the notes below.

Production Budget	Units
Opening inventory of finished goods	43,500
Production	195,000
Sub-total	238,500
Sales	200,000
Closing inventory of finished goods	38,500

(a) Complete these three working schedules.

Materials

Each unit produced requires 0.6 kg of material.

Closing inventory will be valued at the budgeted purchase price.

Materials	kg	£
Opening inventory	30,000	24,000
Purchases	120,000	102,000 = 0·85 X
Sub-total	150,000	126,000
Used in production	117000	97950
Closing inventory	33000	28050

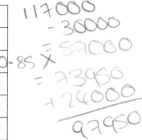

$$117000$$
$$- 30000$$
$$= 87000$$
$$= 73950$$
$$+ 24000$$
$$97950$$

Labour

Each item takes six minutes to produce. 120 staff each work 150 basic hours in the period. Overtime is paid at 1/3 above the basic hourly rate.

Labour	Hours	£
Basic time at £15 per hour	18000	270,000
Overtime	1500	30,000
Total	19500	300,000

$$195000 \times 6/60 = 19500 \text{ hrs}$$
$$120 \times 150 = 18000$$

Overheads

Variable overheads are recovered on total labour hours.

Overheads	Hours	£
Variable overheads at £5 per hour	19500	97500
Fixed overheads		323,550
Total overheads		421050

(b) Now complete the operating budget. Enter all amounts as positive figures. Closing finished goods inventory will be valued at the budgeted production cost per unit.

Operating Budget	Units	£ per unit	£
Sales revenue	260,000	7.00	1,400,000
Cost of goods sold			£
Opening inventory of finished goods			174,000
Cost of production		£	
Materials		97950	
Labour		300000	
Overhead		421050	819000
Closing inventory of finished goods			161700
Cost of goods sold			831300
Gross profit			966700
Non-production overheads		£	
Administration		253,100	
Marketing		120,500	373,600
Operating profit			195100

819000 | 1145000 × 365500 = 161700

(c) Complete the cash flow forecast using the budget data that you have calculated in parts (a) and (b) of this task and the additional information below.

Enter receipts and payments as positive figures.

- The sales receivables balance is expected to decrease by £12,000
- The materials payable balance is expected to decrease by £4,500
- All other payments are made in the period in which they are incurred
- Production overheads include a depreciation charge of £9,000

Cash flow forecast	£	£
Opening cash balance		6,800
Sales receipts		1,412,000
Payments:		
Materials	166,500	
Direct labour	300,000	
Production overheads	412,050	
Other overheads	373,600	
Capital expenditure	14,000	
Total payments		1,706,150
Closing cash balance		212,650

(d) It has been suggested that the closing inventory for materials could be reduced in the operating budget. The sales and production would remain unchanged from the original schedules and budgets prepared in parts (a), (b), and (c), and the other information provided would be unchanged.

Explain what the impact would be on the schedules and budgets, and also note the implications of maintaining lower materials inventory levels.

Task 3

(a)   Operating report

You are required to complete the monthly operating report below. Flex the budget, calculate variances and show whether each variance is favourable or adverse by denoting adverse variances with minus signs. The original budget and actual results have been entered.

Notes:

Materials, labour and distribution costs are variable.

Energy cost is semi-variable. The variable element is £0.50 per unit.

Equipment hire is a stepped cost, budgeted to increase uniformly at every 20,000 units of production.

Depreciation, marketing and administration costs are fixed.

Original budget		Flexed budget	Actual	Variance
121,000	**Sales volume (units)**		105,000	
£		£	£	£
1,452,000	Sales revenue	1,260,000	1,270,500	10500
	Costs:			
242,000	Materials	210,600	207,900	2100
302,500	Labour	267500	264,600	(2100)
181,500	Distribution	157500	158,550	(1050)
80,000	Energy	77000	78,000	(6000)
91,000	Equipment hire	78000	86,350	(8350)
81,300	Depreciation	81300	82,000	(700)
105,000	Marketing	105000	115,250	(10250)
63,400	Administration	63400	62,800	600
1,146,700	Total costs	1,029,200	1,055,450	(25,750)
305,300	Operating profit (loss)	230300	215,050	(15250)

0.5 × 121000 = 60500 - V/E
80000 - 60500 = 19500 F/E

0.5 × 105000 = 52500
+ 19500 = 72000

(b) Select the appropriate term from the options given to match each of the descriptions.

Descriptions	Term	
Using information about the current performance of an organisation to help create future budgets	Feedback	
	Control action	
	Feedforward	✓
	Goal congruence	
Decision making by individuals that is in their own interests, but not in the interests of the organisation	Participative budgeting	
	Goal congruence	
	Budgetary slack	
	Dysfunctional behaviour	✓

Task 4

A company is planning to manufacture and sell a new product from a separate building. The expected volume is 45,000 units per year, with a selling price of £20 per unit, and a mark-up on total costs of 25%.

The annual costs are expected to be:

Variable costs   £270,000 /45000

Fixed costs   £450,000

Handwritten: 45000 × 20 = 900,000
900,000 × 25%.·
= 6 ... =6

(a) Complete the following table:

	£
Total anticipated sales revenue	900,000
Target total profit	180,000
Target total costs	720,000 / 45000
Target total cost per unit	16

(b) Consideration is being given to increasing the selling price by £2 per unit, while maintaining a mark-up on total costs of 25%. Fixed costs (in total) and variable costs (per unit) remain as before.

Complete the following table, based on this proposal:

	£
Increased selling price per unit	22 ✓
Target total profit per unit	4.40
Target total cost per unit	17.60
Variable costs per unit	6 ✓
Target fixed costs per unit	11.60
Target sales volume (to nearest unit)	38794

Handwritten right side:
990,000
25%
270000
450000

Handwritten bottom:
£22 = 125% ∴ 1% = 0.176
25% = £4.40

Sales price 125%
Cost 100%
Profit 25%

(c) Write a brief report that explains the results of your calculations in parts (a) and (b).

(d) Explain briefly how value engineering can be used in conjunction with target costing to meet the needs of both the producer and the customer.

Task 5

A company makes two products, the Esse and the Tee, both using the same materials and the same labour.

The key details are as follows:

	Esse	Tee
Contribution per unit	£80	£60
Materials per unit	2 kg	1 kg
Labour time per unit	2 hours	3 hours

For the coming period, there will be a maximum amount of material available of 10,000 kg. The maximum labour available will be 12,000 hours.

(a) Calculate the contribution per kg of material and the contribution per labour hour for each product, using the following table.

	Esse £	Tee £
Contribution per kg material	40	60
Contribution per labour hour	40	20

(b) Complete the following table with figures to show the simultaneous equations, where S is number of Esses, and T is number of Tees.

Material constraint	2	S	+	1	T	=	10,000
Labour constraint	2	S	+	3	T	=	12000

(c) Complete the following table to show how total contribution can be maximised. Show the production, the materials required, the labour hours required, and the total contribution for each product and in total.

	Esse	Tee	Total
Production (units)			
Materials required (kg)			
Labour required (hours)			
Contribution £			

(d) Calculate the capacity constraints for product FX by completing the table below. Round down to the maximum whole number of units if necessary.

According to the standard cost card, each unit of FX requires 3.6 kilograms of material, 15 minutes of direct labour time and 6 minutes of machine time.

Budgets have been drafted which show the following:

Maximum sales demand of 1,000 units

Material available of 3,450 kilograms

Baoio rate direct labour available (excluding overtime) of 220 hours

Machine time available of 130 hours.

Production capacity	Units
Based on material available	
Based on direct labour hours (without overtime)	
Based on available machine time	
Maximum sales volume, without using overtime	
Maximum sales volume, using unlimited overtime	

Task 6

A company is considering purchasing a new machine that will reduce the labour required to manufacture its products. The details are as follows:

- The machine will cost £350,000, plus installation costs of £25,000 and will have a life of 4 years with no residual value.

- Running costs of the machine are £20,000 per year, payable in arrears.

- Labour costs are £12 per hour, and the machine would save 2 hours labour time in the manufacture of each unit (treat savings as being made annually in arrears).

- Production over the next 4 years is planned to be as follows, starting immediately:

  - Year 1   4,000

  - Year 2   5,000

  - Year 3   5,000

  - Year 4   6,000

The company's cost of capital is 5%.

(a) Complete the following table to calculate the net present value of the project.

Year	Details	Cash Savings £'000	Cash Outflow £'000	Discount Factor 5%	Present Value £'000
0	Cost of machine and installation			1.000	
1	Running costs				
	Labour savings				
	Year 1 net savings			0.952	
2	Running costs				
	Labour savings				
	Year 2 net savings			0.907	
3	Running costs				
	Labour savings				
	Year 3 net savings			0.864	
4	Running costs				
	Labour savings				
	Year 4 net savings			0.823	
		Net present value			

(b) Complete the following statements:

Based on the calculations in part (a), the machine should

be purchased / not be purchased

If the cost of capital were higher, the purchase of the machine would be

more viable / less viable

If the future labour costs were higher, the purchase of the machine would be

more viable / less viable

Task 7

Cosy Hotels Limited operates a number of small hotels. One of its competitors is Lush Hotels. You have been given the following information about Cosy Hotels and Lush Hotels for the year just ended.

Income Statement	Cosy	Lush
	£	£
Revenue	1,312,500	1,680,000
Variable costs		
Food	350,000	432,000
Laundry	87,500	120,000
Cleaning	262,500	288,000
Total variable costs	700,000	840,000
Contribution	**612,500**	**840,000**
Selling and marketing costs	300,000	350,000
Administration costs	155,000	163,000
Financial costs	85,000	118,000
Operating profit	**72,500**	**209,000**

Other information	Cosy	Lush
Number of room-nights occupied	17,500	24,000
Number of room-nights available	35,000	30,000

(a) Calculate the performance indicators to complete the following table for Cosy Hotels and Lush Hotels:

Give answers to two decimal places.

	Cosy	Lush
Selling price per room-night £		
Occupancy rate %		
Variable costs per room-night £		
Contribution per room-night £		
Contribution / sales ratio %		
Operating profit margin %		
Selling and marketing cost as % of sales		

(b) Analyse the performance of Cosy Hotels, compared to Lush Hotels, using the indicators calculated in part (a).

Task 8

(a) From the following statements regarding managing divisional performance, select those that are true.

Statement	True ✔
When calculating return on investment for a division, the operating profit used should be that which is controllable by the divisional managers	
Transfer pricing should never be set at a level lower than the full absorption cost of the selling division	
When calculating residual income, the percentage applied to the investment should be set by the managers in the head office, based on the cost of capital of the whole organisation	
Transfer pricing should never be set at a level lower than the marginal cost of the selling division	
Setting a transfer price at the marginal cost of the selling division may reduce the profitability of that division and demotivate its managers	
Setting a transfer price at market price can never be appropriate as it will demotivate the purchasing divisional managers	
Setting a transfer price at market price may be appropriate if the selling division has a ready market for all its production	

(b) A raw material has had the following cost per kilo over the last few months:

	June	July	August
Cost per kilo	£531.26	£533.60	£535.94

Complete the following table with the expected cost per kilo later the same year:

	October	November
Cost per kilo		

(c) The formula for linear regression for the cost of a certain raw material has been calculated as:

$y = 44.1x + 2,391.5$

'y' is the cost per tonne in £ and 'x' is the period.

August 20-4 was period 25.

Complete the following sentence:

The forecast cost per tonne in December 20-4 is £ ⬚ to the nearest penny.

Practice
assessment 3

Task 1

(a) Match the data in the first column with the appropriate source in the second column.

Data
Customers who pay promptly
Current raw materials costs
Employers' National Insurance rates

Source
Product life cycle report
Office for National Statistics
HMRC website
Sales ledger
Supplier price lists
Trade association

(b) Who would you contact in each of the following situations?

(a)	You want to know details of expected future material costs	4
(b)	You want to know when the factory extension will be operational	1
(c)	You want to know the cost of next year's advertising campaign	6

Select from:

1 Factory Capital Project Manager

2 HR Manager

3 Transport Manager

4 Purchasing Manager

5 Finance Director

6 Marketing Manager

(c) Complete the following table by using ticks to show into which budget(s) each item of cost would occur.

	Capital expenditure	Cost of production	Sales and marketing	Distribution	Finance
Loan set up fees					✓
Celebrity product endorsement fees			✓		
Product design royalties		✓			
Purchase of new distribution vehicle	✓				
Agency fees for temporary production labour		✓			
Distribution vehicle fuel				✓	

(d) Select an appropriate accounting treatment for each of the following costs from the options available.

Descriptions:

(a)	Employers' pension contributions for sales staff	2
(b)	Product design royalties	3
(c)	Repairs to factory roof	1
(d)	Cost of maintaining production equipment	1
(e)	Cost of sick pay for production operatives	1
(f)	Cost of advertising campaign	5

Options are:

1   Allocate to production overheads

2   Allocate to selling and distribution overheads

3   Direct cost

4   Allocate to finance overheads

5   Allocate to marketing overheads

6   Capital expenditure

Task 2

(a)   You have prepared a draft budget for direct labour costs.

- The budget is based on the expected rise in the relevant regional labour cost index of 2.2%, although the company wage negotiations for next year have not yet concluded. This information has been provided by the HR Manager.

- The Production Manager has confirmed that an efficiency saving of 1% of the labour time required to make each unit is expected due to replacement of some production machinery that is scheduled for the end of the current year.

- In the current year the direct labour hours have been fulfilled by full time employees, who did not work any overtime.

- You have calculated the total labour hours required from the agreed production budget.

- You have been asked to suggest possible inherent risks in the draft budget and its assumptions.

Direct labour budget	This year actual	Next year's budget
Production units	450,000	440,000
Labour time required to produce 1,000 units	50	49.5
Total labour hours required	22,500	21,780
Hourly rate	£12.50	£12.775
Total labour cost	£281,250	£278,240

Write an email to the Production Director:

- Explaining the calculations and assumptions.

- Suggesting possible inherent risks in the draft budget and its assumptions.

Email

To:

From:

Date:

Subject:

(b) Department W manufactures three products, Exe, Wye and Zed.

Calculate the machine hours required to manufacture these in November, using the following table.

Product	Units	Hours per unit	Hours required
Exe	450	2.0	900
Wye	570	1.2	684
Zed	400	1.0	400
Total machine hours for department W			1984

There are seven machines in the department. X290 = 2030 hrs

Each machine can be used for 290 hours in November. Additional machines can be hired if required.

How many additional machines should be hired?   none

(c) Calculate the capacity constraints for product GT by completing the table below. Round down to the maximum whole number of units if necessary.

According to the standard cost card, each unit of GT requires 4.1 kilograms of material, 66 minutes of direct labour time and 15 minutes of machine time.

Budgets have been drafted which show the following:

Maximum sales demand of 1,500 units

Material available of 6,050 kilograms

Basic rate direct labour available (excluding overtime) of 1,480 hours

Machine time available of 350 hours

Production capacity	Units
Based on material available	1475
Based on direct labour hours (without overtime)	1345
Based on available machine time	1400
Maximum sales volume, without using overtime	1345
Maximum sales volume, using unlimited overtime	1400

1500 x 66 x 60 = 1650 hrs

Task 3

(a) Select the appropriate term from the options given to match the description.

Description	Term	
The standard cost variance that records the difference between the flexed direct labour budget and the actual cost of direct labour	Total direct cost variance	
	Direct labour rate variance	
	Direct labour cost variance	✓
	Direct material efficiency variance	

(b) The operating statement for September showed that the direct raw material costs were £57,850. 15,974 kilos of material were used and 9,800 items were produced. The standard cost allows 1.6 kilos of material for each item, at a standard price of £3.60 per kilo.

Complete the following table, and show whether each variance is favourable or adverse.

Direct raw material costs	1·6 X 3·6 X 9800 =	Fav / Adv
Flexed budget (standard cost)	£ 56448	
Actual price per kilo (to £0.01)	£ 3·62	
Actual material used per item	1·63 kg	
Price variance (to nearest £)	£ 344	Adv
Usage variance (to nearest £)	£ 1058	Adv
Cost variance	£ 1402	Adv
Cost variance % (to 0.01 %)	2·48 %	

57850 - 56448 = 1402

3·60 × 15974 = 57506

(c) Prepare the direct labour cost statement from the activity data provided.

Round to the nearest whole number if necessary. Show adverse variances as negative amounts.

Activity data	Items produced	Labour hours	Cost
			£
Budget	24,300	8,100	170,100
Actual results	23,700	8,000	165,900

) 100

Direct labour cost statement	£
Standard labour cost of production	165900
Labour rate variance	2100
Labour efficiency variance	-2100
Labour cost variance	0

Task 4

A company manufactures two products, Eff and Gee. The two overhead activities, production set-ups and materials handling have budgets of £240,000 and £360,000 respectively.

The following table provides additional information.

	Eff	Gee
Direct materials per unit	£10.00	£15.00
Direct labour per unit at £20 / hr	£40.00	£25.00
Number of production set-ups	50	100
Number of material requisitions	240	120
Budgeted production units	25,000	8,000

Handwritten annotations: "2" beside Direct labour row; "1·25" beside £25.00; "150" beside 100; "360" beside 120

(a) Complete the following table, using Activity Based Costing principles. Round per unit figures to the nearest penny.

Cost driver – per production set-up £	240,000 /150 = 1600	
Cost driver – per requisition £	360,000 /360 = 1000	
	Eff £	**Gee £**
Total production set-up cost	80,000	160,000
Set-up cost per unit	3·20	20
Total materials handling cost	240,000	120,000
Materials handling cost per unit	9·60	15

(b) Calculate total fixed overheads if they were absorbed on a budgeted labour hour basis, using the following table.

Budgeted labour hours	60,000	
Overhead absorption rate £	10	
	Eff £	**Gee £**
Overheads per unit	20	12·50
Total overheads absorbed	500,000	100,000

(c) Using the information from (a) and (b) calculate the total cost per unit, using ABC and absorption using labour hours. Round amounts to the nearest penny.

	Eff £	**Gee £**
Total cost per unit using ABC	67·80	75
Total cost per unit using absorption costing	70	52·50

Handwritten: 800

(d) Explain very briefly the impact that using overheads absorbed on a budgeted labour hour basis could have on decisions concerning the two products.

Task 5

Gamma Limited manufactures a food paste that is currently sold in jars and is considering launching a more concentrated version to replace the current product. It will be sold in small tubes.

- Current sales volume is 3.0 million units per annum and this is not expected to change.
- Current fixed production costs are £0.7 million.
- Current labour cost per unit is £0.55 which is completely variable.
- Current material cost per unit is £0.95 and is completely variable.
- Assume stock levels are kept at zero.
- Variable material cost of the new product will be £0.15 less per unit than the current food product.
- Selling price will be increased from £2.60 to £2.70.
- Fixed selling and distribution costs will reduce from £400,000 to £250,000.
- Additional investment in assets will be £4 million which will be depreciated at £400,000 per annum.
- All other costs will remain the same.

[handwritten annotations:]
$2.70 - 1.35 =$
1.35

| 0.55 |
| 0.95 |
| (0.15) | / 1.35

≈ 0.10

$(150,000)$

→ Fixed
400,000

(a) Calculate the total annual increase in profit by completing the table below.

	Units	Price/cost	Total £
Additional revenue	3,000,000	0.10	300,000
Savings on materials	3,000,000	0.15	450,000
Reduction in selling and distribution costs			150,000
Additional depreciation			(400,000)
Additional annual profit			500,000

(b) Based on the new product, calculate the performance measures shown in the following table to help understand any additional risk.

Return on additional initial investment (%)	500,000 / 4000,000 ×100 = 12.5%
Total fixed costs *[0.7m + 0.25m + £0.4]*	£1.35 million
Contribution per unit *[→ SP − VC =]*	£1.35

[handwritten:] 300,000 —

(c) Select one of the following techniques that could also be used to help in decision-making regarding the new product.

Technique	✔
Activity Based Costing	
Standard Costing Variance Analysis	
Discounted Cash Flow Net Present Value	✓
Trend Analysis with Seasonal Variations	

Task 6

EyeTee Technologies Ltd is considering developing a new games console. The following data has been collected regarding this new product.

Development costs (including creating prototypes) are expected to be £1,200,000, spread evenly over years 0, 1 and 2. = 400

Production unit numbers and sales numbers are planned as follows:

	Production	Sales	VC	FC	SP
Year 2	10,000	0	800	140	
Year 3	40,000	40,000	3200	140	600
Year 4	50,000	50,000	4000	140	750
Year 5	20,000	30,000	1600	140	4 200

No production or sales are expected after year 5.

Variable costs of production are budgeted at £80 per unit. Fixed production costs are budgeted at £140,000 for each of the years 2 to 5.

Selling prices are planned at £150 per unit for sales in years 3 and 4, reducing to £140 per unit in year 5.

The company's cost of capital is 10%, and this is reflected in the discount factors given below.

(a) Complete the following table to calculate both the non-discounted and discounted life-cycle cash flows for the product. Round to the nearest £000.

Year	Cash Inflow £000	Cash Outflow £000	Net Cash Flow £000	Discount Factor	Present Value £000
0	0	400	−400	1.000	−400
1	0	400	−400	0.909	−364
2	0	1340	−1340	0.826	−1107
3	6000	3340	2660	0.751	1998
4	7500	4140	3360	0.683	2295
5	4200	1740	2460	0.621	1528
	Totals				3950

(b) From the following list of situations that differ from the initial assumptions, analyse between those that will tend to make the project more viable, and those that will make it less viable.

Situation	More Viable	Less Viable
Cost of capital is lower than 10%	✓	
Development costs are greater than £1,200,000		✓
Increased competition affects sales volume		✓
Product life cycle is extended, and additional sales are generated in year 6	✓	
Product becomes obsolete more quickly than planned		✓
Increased competition affects selling price		✓
Cost of capital is greater than 10%		✓

Task 7

Eye Limited is comparing its results with its major competitor Jay plc. You have been given the following information about Eye and Jay for the year just ended.

Statement of Profit or Loss	Eye	Jay
	£000	£000
Sales revenue	36,000	57,200
Cost of production		
Direct (raw) materials	8,000	13,650
Direct labour	7,200	11,375
Fixed production overheads	5,000	9,000
Total cost of production	20,200	34,025
Gross profit	**15,800**	**23,175**
Selling and distribution costs	4,000	7,100
Administration costs	3,250	4,800
Advertising costs	4,200	5,500
Operating profit	**4,350**	**5,775**

Other information		Eye	Jay
Number of units sold	**Units**	4,000,000	6,500,000
Capital employed	(£000)	65,000	95,000

(a) Calculate the performance indicators to complete the following table for Eye Ltd and Jay plc:

Give answers to two decimal places.

	Eye Ltd	Jay plc
Selling price per unit	9.00	8.80
Direct material cost per unit	2.00	2.10
Direct labour cost per unit	1.80	1.75
Fixed production overheads per unit	1.25	1.38
Gross profit margin	43.89.%	40.52%
Operating profit margin	12.08%	10.09%
Administration cost as % of turnover	9.03%	8.39%
Return on capital employed	6.69%	6.08%

(b) Analyse the performance of Eye Ltd in comparison with Jay plc, making reference to the indicators calculated in part (a). Also suggest any action that you consider it may be appropriate for Eye Ltd to undertake to improve its performance.

Task 8

(a) The following data relates to the prices per kilogram of a type of fruit. Complete the table by inserting the seasonal variations, including + or − signs.

	March	April	May
Actual price	£1.30	£1.25	£1.10
Trend	£1.28	£1.30	£1.32
Seasonal variation	+0.02	−0.05	+0.22

(b) A formula has been developed to estimate the future trend in vehicle prices.

It is based on the equation $y = mx + c$, where

y   is the expected price for a specific type of vehicle in the future

m   is a constant £25

x   is the month number of the required future date, counting from the base month of January 2016 (ie January 2016 is month 0)   DeC 16   11

c   is a constant £14,000   DeC 17   23

Calculate the expected vehicle price in October 2018.   Oct 18   33

£ | 14,825 |

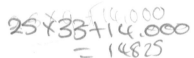

$25 \times 33 + 14,000$
$= 14825$

(c) Calculate the 3 month moving averages for the following sales volume data:

Month	Sales volume	3 month moving average
January	57,000	
February	58,000	57500
March	57,500	58500
April	60,000	59500
May	61,000	60500
June	60,500	61500
July	63,000	

Answers to practice assessment 1

Task 1

(a)

Descriptions	Term	
Budgets that are continually extended into the future as time moves forward	Incremental budgets	
	Flexible budgets	
	Rolling budgets	✔
	Activity based budgets	

(b) (a) 5

   (b) 4

   (c) 1

(c)

	Direct cost of production	Production overheads	Capital expenditure	Marketing	Cash
Extension to offices			✔		✔
Depreciation of production equipment		✔			
Indirect production labour		✔			✔
Advertising campaign costs				✔	✔
Hire of production equipment		✔			✔
Printing customer perceptions questionnaire				✔	✔

(d) (a) 2

   (b) 3

   (c) 2

   (d) 1

   (e) 6

   (f) 3

Task 2

(a)

	Month 1	Month 2	Month 3
Required units	75,330	79,980	77,190
Manufactured units	81,000	86,000	83,000

(b)   The number of units that can be made in basic time during October is **43,200**.

The number of overtime hours required to be worked in October is **340**.

(c)   There is labour available to make **52,500** units in normal time. Therefore, **2,500** hours of overtime will be needed.

The raw material contract will provide enough material to make **40,000** units. Therefore, **50,000** kg will have to be purchased on the open market.

Quality control can test **50,400** units in the year. It will be necessary to make alternative arrangements for **9,600** units.

(d)   **(i)**

Operating budget	First scenario	Alternative scenario
Selling price per unit	£15.00	£14.70
Sales volume	130,000	140,400
	£	£
Sales revenue	1,950,000	2,063,880
Costs:		
Materials	585,000	631,800
Labour	390,000	421,200
Depreciation	180,000	180,000
Energy	115,000	122,925
Occupancy costs	189,400	197,923
Total costs	1,459,400	1,553,848
Operating profit	490,600	510,032
Increase / (decrease) in profit		19,432

(ii)

> The alternative scenario shows an increase in profits of £19,432 compared with the first scenario. While some of the assumptions can be verified, there may be others that are less certain.
>
> The selling price per unit will be in the control of the organisation, however, the increase in sales volume is less certain. It may have been arrived at as a result of market research, but even if it is slightly inaccurate, it will have a major impact on the results.
>
> Materials and labour have been assumed to behave as variable costs, but that may be a simplification. There may be additional costs arising from overtime working, or there may be savings due to additional discounts from purchasing a greater quantity of material.
>
> It seems likely that the assumption regarding depreciation is a valid one, since the organisation will be aware of how that has been arrived at.
>
> If the assumptions regarding energy cost behaviour and the likely price increase have been developed in conjunction with the energy supplier, then this should be quite reliable.
>
> There is insufficient information currently available to determine how reliable the assumption regarding occupancy costs is. It will depend on how this assumption has been developed, and why a fixed cost will be expected to increase.

Task 3

(a)

Description	Term	
The difference between the expected and actual cost of direct materials that is due to using a different quantity of materials than standard	Direct material price variance	
	Direct material usage variance	✔
	Direct material cost variance	
	Direct material efficiency variance	

(b)

Direct raw material costs		Fav / Adv
Flexed budget (standard cost)	£25,520	
Actual price per kilo (to £0.01)	£8.15	
Actual material used per item	0.6 kg	
Price variance	£495	Adv
Usage variance	£880	Adv
Cost variance	£1,375	Adv
Cost variance % (to 0.1 %)	5.4%	

(c)

Direct labour cost statement	£
Standard labour cost of production	126,000
Labour rate variance	3,500
Labour efficiency variance	0
Labour cost variance	3,500

Task 4

(a)

Cost driver – per material requisition £		4,000	
Cost driver – per production set-up £		8,000	
		Alpha £	**Delta £**
Total materials handling cost		700,000	2,800,000
Total production set-up cost		400,000	1,600,000

(b)

Budgeted labour hours	275,000	
Overhead absorption rate £	20	
	Alpha £	**Delta £**
Overheads per unit	40	20
Total overheads absorbed	3,500,000	2,000,000

(c)

The traditional way of absorbing fixed overheads on a budgeted labour hour basis is an arbitrary method, since labour hours may bear little relationship to what causes the overhead costs.

Activity based costing attempts to examine the causes of groups of overhead cost (cost pools) and uses these activities (the cost drivers) to distribute the costs to the products. In this way, the product which uses the most cost will be charged the most. This provides more accurate product costs that will assist management decision making.

(d)

Cloud accounting involves a business's software and date being held remotely away from the business premises. This is carried out via an IT provider. Software that is available will include all usual accounting packages, together with, for example, inventory management and activity based costing.

The advantages of the system include the following:

Staff that have the necessary clearance can access the data in real time from any location, including home working.

Costs of capital expenditure on hardware and software are normally avoided, along with some (but not all) costs of in-house IT staff.

Automatic software updates will normally be provided by the IT provider.

The amount of data that can be stored is virtually limitless.

The main disadvantages include:

Tying the organisation to an IT provider which may be difficult to disentangle in the future.

Payment based on subscription or usage may be higher than an equivalent in-house facility.

Security of the data is in the hands of the IT provider, and any breach may be catastrophic for the business or its customers.

Task 5

(a)

	Chef	Field
Total direct materials required (kg)	20,000	45,000
Total direct labour required (hours)	20,000	15,000
Contribution per unit £	24	30
Contribution per limiting factor £ (to 2 d.p.)	12.00	10.00
Optimal production (units)	10,000	10,000

(b)

	£
15,000 kg of additional material	150,000
5,000 hours of additional labour	0

(c)

Statement	True ✔
Linear programming can only be used when there is a single constraint	
Linear programming assumes that the contribution per unit of each product remains constant, regardless of the volume produced	✔
Linear programming can usually be carried out using simultaneous equations or a graph	✔
Linear programming can be used where there are two products and two or more constraints	✔
Linear programming can only be used where there is a single product	
Linear programming assumes that the amount of resources required per unit of each product remains constant, regardless of the volume produced	✔
Linear programming ignores fixed costs	✔

Task 6

(a)

Year	Cash Flow	Disc Factor 10%	Disc Cash Flow 10%
0	−8,500,000	1.000	−8,500,000
1	2,500,000	0.909	2,272,500
2	2,500,000	0.826	2,065,000
3	2,500,000	0.751	1,877,500
4	2,500,000	0.683	1,707,500
5	2,500,000	0.621	1,552,500
Net Present Value			975,000

(b)   The payback period, to the nearest year is 3 years

(c)   The discounted payback period, to the nearest year is 4 years

(d)   The estimated internal rate of return to one decimal place is calculated as 10% + 5% (975,000 / (975,000 + 117,500))= 14.5%

(e)   The accounting rate of return to the nearest whole %, using the average investment is calculated as (£800,000 / £4,250,000) x 100   = 19%

Task 7

(a)

	Scenario 1	Scenario 2
Gross Profit margin	20.00%	24.87%
Operating profit margin	8.33%	13.65%
Direct Materials as a percentage of turnover	20.00%	23.08%
Direct Materials cost per unit	£3.00	£3.00
Direct labour cost per unit	£2.00	£2.10
Fixed production cost per unit	£7.00	£4.67

(b)

Although the sales volume in scenario 2 is 50% greater than in scenario 1, this, itself does not affect the gross profit margin (as a percentage). As noted later the increased volume does however spread the fixed costs over more units. The margin is affected by the selling price which is £2 per unit less in scenario 2. This has the effect of reducing the gross profit margin as a percentage.

The material cost is the same per unit in each scenario, since it behaves as a variable cost. This therefore has no impact on the gross profit margin.

The labour cost per unit is slightly higher when the volume is greater. This could be due (for example) to the use of overtime working. The impact on the gross profit margin is to reduce it slightly in scenario 2.

The fixed production costs form a large part of the cost of production. Since the volume is much higher in scenario 2, the fixed production cost per unit is significantly lower. This has the effect of improving the gross profit margin, and this is the main factor in the difference between the margins. It more than compensates for the impact of selling price and labour costs.

The operating profit margin in scenario 2 is influenced by the gross profit margin, which is better than that in scenario 1, as discussed above. It also benefits from selling and distribution costs that appear to be semi-variable, and administration costs that behave as a fixed cost.

Provided the situation outlined in scenario 2 is thought to be achievable, then this should be followed, since it provides more than twice the operating profit of scenario 1. This is due to the economies of scale that impact on the fixed costs within the business.

However, before finalising a decision, particular care should be taken to examine the sales units forecast under scenario 2, because if this is flawed then the selling price reduction could easily lead to a worse operating profit than in scenario 1.

Task 8

(a)

Period	Actual data / Forecast data	3 point moving averages (Trend)	Seasonal variations
30	1,060		
31	1,095	1,070	+25
32	1,055	1,090	−35
33	1,120	1,110	+10
34	1,155	1,130	+25
35	1,115	1,150	−35
36	1,180		
37	1,215	1,190	+25
38	1,175	1,210	−35
39	1,240	1,230	+10
40	1,275	1,250	+25

(b)

Month	Actual costs £	RPI	Costs at January prices £
January	115,600	246	115,600
May	118,500	250	116,604
October	119,000	252	116,167

(c) 'a' = £6,000

'b' = £10

Workings:

Difference in costs and units of given figures are £10,000, and 1,000 units.

Therefore variable cost per unit is:

£10,000 / 1,000 units = £10 – this is 'b' in the equation

The total cost 'y' for 500 units is £11,000.

Of this 'bx' is equal to £10 multiplied by 500 = £5,000

There 'a' must be the remaining cost (£11,000 – £5,000) = £6,000.

This is the fixed cost.

Note: this calculation is identical to the high-low method.

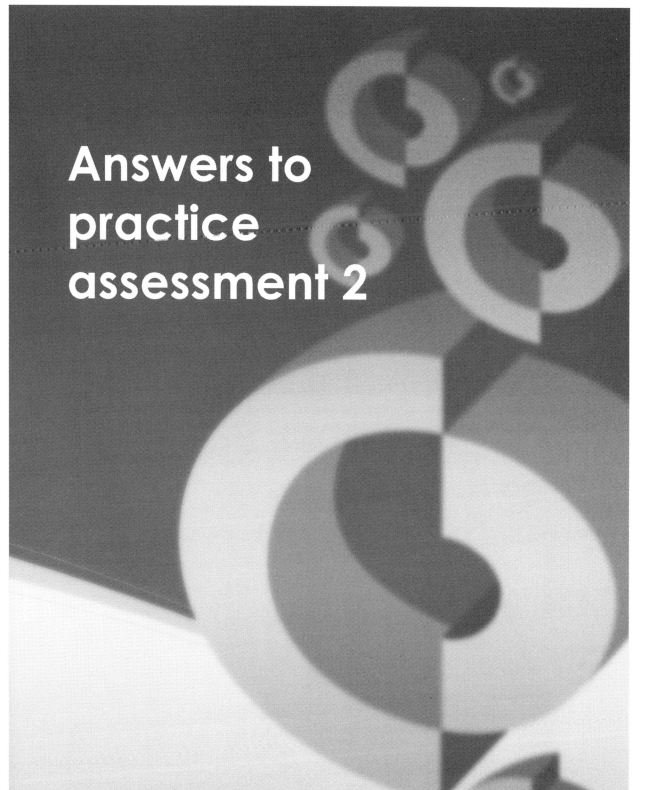

Answers to practice assessment 2

Task 1

(a)

Data		Source
Amount of planned dividend payment	⟶	Minutes of board meeting
Details planned output levels	⟶	Production schedules
Demographic details of locality	⟶	Office for National Statistics

(b)   (a)   5

      (b)   1

      (c)   4

(c)   (a)   2

      (b)   1

      (c)   6

      (d)   3

      (e)   4

      (f)   6

      (g)   1

      (h)   2

(d)   (a)   6

      (b)   9

      (c)   7

      (d)   11

      (e)   3

(e)

Description	Term	
The manager responsible for a specific budget and the actual performance that is measured against that budget	Budget accountant	
	Budget holder	✔
	Budget committee	
	Budget manual	

Task 2

(a)

Materials

Materials	kg	£
Opening inventory	30,000	24,000
Purchases	120,000	102,000
Sub-total	150,000	126,000
Used in production	117,000	97,950
Closing inventory	33,000	28,050

Labour

Labour	Hours	£
Basic time at £15 per hour	18,000	270,000
Overtime	1,500	30,000
Total	19,500	300,000

Overheads

Overhead	Hours	£
Variable overheads at £5 per hour	19,500	97,500
Fixed overheads		323,550
Total overheads		421,050

(b)

Operating Budget	Units	£ per unit	£
Sales revenue	200,000	7.00	1,400,000
Cost of goods sold			£
Opening inventory of finished goods			174,000
Cost of production		£	
Materials		97,950	
Labour		300,000	
Overhead		421,050	819,000
Closing inventory of finished goods			161,700
Cost of goods sold			831,300
Gross profit			568,700
Non-production overheads		£	
Administration		253,100	
Marketing		120,500	373,600
Operating profit			195,100

(c)

Cash flow forecast	£	£
Opening cash balance		6,800
Sales receipts		1,412,000
Payments:		
Materials	106,500	
Direct labour	300,000	
Production overheads	412,050	
Other overheads	373,600	
Capital expenditure	14,000	
Total payments		1,206,150
Closing cash balance		212,650

(d)

> If the closing inventory of materials was reduced in the operating budget, then purchases of materials would need to be reduced, since the original quantity and cost of materials would be used in production. The reduction in inventory of materials would be the same as the reduction in purchases for the period.
>
> The cost of materials that form part of the cost of production in the operating budget would be unchanged, and therefore the budgeted operating profit would also be unchanged.
>
> Regarding the cash flow forecast, the payments for materials would be reduced compared with the original forecast. This would increase the closing cash balance by the same amount as the reduction in cost of the closing materials inventory.
>
> If lower materials inventory were maintained, then the reduction could be translated into higher cash balances or utilised in other ways. However, a lower materials inventory level would also increase the risk of running out of materials, especially if there were either a surge in sales demand, or a supply problem.

Task 3

(a)

Original budget		Flexed budget	Actual	Variance
121,000	**Sales volume (units)**		105,000	
£		£	£	£
1,452,000	Sales revenue	1,260,000	1,270,500	10,500
	Costs:			
242,000	Materials	210,000	207,900	2,100
302,500	Labour	262,500	264,600	–2,100
181,500	Distribution	157,500	158,550	–1,050
80,000	Energy	72,000	78,000	–6,000
91,000	Equipment hire	78,000	86,350	–8,350
81,300	Depreciation	81,300	82,000	–700
105,000	Marketing	105,000	115,250	–10,250
63,400	Administration	63,400	62,800	600
1,146,700	Total costs	1,029,700	1,055,450	–25,750
305,300	Operating profit (loss)	230,300	215,050	–15,250

(b)

Descriptions	Term	
Using information about the current performance of an organisation to help create future budgets	Feedback	
	Control action	
	Feedforward	✔
	Goal congruence	
Decision making by individuals that is in their own interests, but not in the interests of the organisation	Participative budgeting	
	Goal congruence	
	Budgetary slack	
	Dysfunctional behaviour	✔

Task 4

(a)

	£
Total anticipated sales revenue	900,000
Target total profit	180,000
Target total costs	720,000
Target total cost per unit	16.00

(b)

	£
Increased selling price per unit	22.00
Target total profit per unit	4.40
Target total cost per unit	17.60
Variable costs per unit	6.00
Target fixed costs per unit	11.60
Target sales volume (to nearest unit)	38,793

(c)

> In the original scenario the target costs equalled the expected costs based on a selling price of £20 per unit, sales volume of 45,000 units and a mark-up on total costs of 25%.
>
> This is because the total costs made up of variable costs of £270,000 and fixed costs of £450,000 equals £720,000, which is equivalent to £16.00 per unit target costs multiplied by 45,000 expected volume.
>
> In the second scenario the increased selling price allows a higher target profit per unit and a higher target cost per unit, based on maintaining the 25% mark-up. Since the variable cost per unit does not change, this produces an increased target fixed cost per unit, which translates into a lower sales volume of 38,793 to achieve target.
>
> It should be noted that the target total profit in the second scenario is lower than the first. This is because although it is based on a higher profit per unit of £4.40 (compared with £20.00 - £16.00 = £4.00), the target volume of 38,793 is lower. This means that the target total profit is only 38,793 x £4.40 = £170,689 compared with the original target profit of £180,000.

(d)

> Value engineering is concerned with ensuring that quality is built into products without unnecessary costs that do not add value. This should result in the lowest cost for a particular product design. If this cost also meets the target cost, then this design should be acceptable. If it does not meet the target cost, then further work would be required on alternative designs or product specification.
>
> Success in using value engineering alongside target costing should result in the following:
> - The consumers are satisfied that the product meets their needs in terms of value in use and prestige value.
> - Sufficient consumers are willing to pay the price that the producer wishes to set, so that the target market share is met.
> - The product costs and profits are at target level.

Task 5

(a)

	Esse £	Tee £
Contribution per kg material	40	60
Contribution per labour hour	40	20

(b)

Material constraint	2	S	+	1	T	=	10,000
Labour constraint	2	S	+	3	T	=	12,000

(c)

	Esse	Tee	Total
Production (units)	4,500	1,000	5,500
Materials required (kg)	9,000	1,000	10,000
Labour required (hours)	9,000	3,000	12,000
Contribution £	360,000	60,000	420,000

(d)

Production capacity	Units
Based on material available	958
Based on direct labour hours (without overtime)	880
Based on available machine time	1,300
Maximum sales volume, without using overtime	880
Maximum sales volume, using unlimited overtime	958

Task 6

(a)

Year	Details	Cash Savings £'000	Cash Outflow £'000	Discount Factor 5%	Present Value £'000
0	Cost of machine and installation		375,000	1.000	(375,000)
1	Running costs		20,000		
	Labour savings	96,000			
	Year 1 net savings	76,000		0.952	72,352
2	Running costs		20,000		
	Labour savings	120,000			
	Year 2 net savings	100,000		0.907	90,700
3	Running costs		20,000		
	Labour savings	120,000			
	Year 3 net savings	100,000		0.864	86,400
4	Running costs		20,000		
	Labour savings	144,000			
	Year 4 net savings	124,000		0.823	102,052
		Net present value			(23,496)

(b) Based on the calculations in part (a), the machine should

not be purchased

If the cost of capital were higher, the purchase of the machine would be

less viable

If the future labour costs were higher, the purchase of the machine would be

more viable

Task 7

(a)

	Cosy	Lush
Selling price per room-night £	75.00	70.00
Occupancy rate %	50.00	80.00
Variable costs per room-night £	40.00	35.00
Contribution per room-night £	35.00	35.00
Contribution / sales ratio %	46.67	50.00
Operating profit margin %	5.52	12.44
Selling and marketing cost as % of sales	22.86	20.83

(b)

The key indicator that leads to the difference in financial performance of the two hotels is the occupancy rate. Cosy Hotels has an occupancy rate of 50%, whereas Lush Hotels has a much higher occupancy rate of 80%.

Cosy Hotels sells its rooms for an average price of £75 per night, which is slightly higher than the average Lush Hotels price of £70 per night. This may have contributed to the higher occupancy rate of Lush Hotels, assuming the rooms are of comparable quality. Both hotels have the same contribution per room-night of £35, since Cosy Hotels have higher variable costs per room-night than Lush Hotels.

The higher occupancy rate of Lush Hotels leads to a higher total contribution than Cosy Hotels, and a higher contribution to sales ratio. Although the fixed costs of Lush Hotels are higher than those of Cosy Hotels, the higher total contribution of Lush Hotels more than compensates for this. The result is a higher operating profit for Lush Hotels, both in absolute terms, and in operating profit margin, which is more than double its competitor.

It would appear that the selling and marketing policy of Lush Hotels is more effective than that of Cosy Hotels. Lush Hotels spends more in absolute terms, but slightly less as a percentage of sales than Cosy Hotels. As noted earlier, the occupancy rate that derives from the sales and marketing policy is far greater for Lush Hotels.

Task 8

(a)

Statement	True ✔
When calculating return on investment for a division, the operating profit used should be that which is controllable by the divisional managers	✔
Transfer pricing should never be set at a level lower than the full absorption cost of the selling division	
When calculating residual income, the percentage applied to the investment should be set by the managers in the head office, based on the cost of capital of the whole organisation	✔
Transfer pricing should never be set at a level lower than the marginal cost of the selling division	✔
Setting a transfer price at the marginal cost of the selling division may reduce the profitability of that division and demotivate its managers	✔
Setting a transfer price at market price can never be appropriate as it will demotivate the purchasing divisional managers	
Setting a transfer price at market price may be appropriate if the selling division has a ready market for all its production	✔

(b)

	October	November
Cost per kilo	£540.62	£542.96

Workings:

Cost is increasing each month by £2.34.

(c)   The forecast cost per tonne in December 20-4 is **£3,670.40** to the nearest penny.

Workings:

(44.1 x 29) + 2,391.5 = £3,670.40

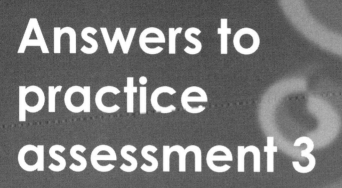

Answers to practice assessment 3

Task 1

(a)

Data		Source
Customers who pay promptly	➡	Sales ledger
Current raw materials costs	➡	Supplier price lists
Employers' National Insurance rates	➡	HMRC website

(b) (a) 4

   (b) 1

   (c) 6

(c)

	Capital expenditure	Cost of production	Sales and marketing	Distribution	Finance
Loan set up fees					✔
Celebrity product endorsement fees			✔		
Product design royalties		✔			
Purchase of new distribution vehicle	✔				
Agency fees for temporary production labour		✔			
Distribution vehicle fuel				✔	

(d) (a) 2

   (b) 3

   (c) 1

   (d) 1

   (e) 1

   (f) 5

Task 2 (a)

Email

To: Production Director

From: Budget Accountant

Date: xx

Subject: Direct Labour Budget

Budget calculations and assumptions

I attach the proposed direct labour budget for next year.

The agreed production plan is based on a reduction in output from 450,000 units this year to 440,000 units next year.

A reduction in the time taken to produce each unit of 1% compared to the current year has been allowed for. This is an anticipated efficiency saving due to the use of some new machinery that is shortly to be installed.

An increase in the current labour rate has been incorporated into the budget. This increase of 2.2% is in line with the forecast regional labour cost index.

The total direct labour cost for next year is £278,240 based on these assumptions.

Please let me know if you need any further information.

Inherent risks

The various assumptions built into the budget could prove to be inaccurate and this would result in risks to the budget. These include:

- The budget is based on 440,000 units being produced. If this forecast is inaccurate then it will impact on the direct labour costs.

- The budget assumes that the direct labour requirement is entirely in proportion to the production level. If there is a part of the labour requirement that does not behave in this way then the hours required may differ from the budget.

- Since the total number of direct labour hours required is fewer than this year there could be costs involved in transferring staff to other duties or even redundancy costs.

- Installation of the planned new machinery could be delayed which would reduce or eliminate the expected efficiency saving of 1%. If the machinery is installed on time the efficiency saving may not be as expected.

- The wage rate increase is based on the expected rise in the regional labour cost index. This index may prove an unreliable estimate of the costs that this company incurs, which will depend on the company wage negotiations which have not yet concluded.

(b)

Product	Units	Hours per unit	Hours required
Exe	450	2.0	900
Wye	570	1.2	684
Zed	400	1.0	400
Total machine hours for department W			1,984

No additional machines should be hired.

(c)

Production capacity	Units
Based on material available	1,475
Based on direct labour hours (without overtime)	1,345
Based on available machine time	1,400
Maximum sales volume, without using overtime	1,345
Maximum sales volume, using unlimited overtime	1,400

Task 3

(a)

Description	Term	
The standard cost variance that records the difference between the flexed direct labour budget and the actual cost of direct labour	Total direct cost variance	
	Direct labour rate variance	
	Direct labour cost variance	✔
	Direct material efficiency variance	

(b)

Direct raw material costs		Fav / Adv
Flexed budget (standard cost)	£56,448	
Actual price per kilo (to £0.01)	£3.62	
Actual material used per item	1.63 kg	
Price variance (to nearest £)	£344	Adv
Usage variance (to nearest £)	£1,058	Adv
Cost variance	£1,402	Adv
Cost variance % (to 0.01 %)	2.48%	

(c)

Direct labour cost statement	£
Standard labour cost of production	165,900
Labour rate variance	2,100
Labour efficiency variance	−2,100
Labour cost variance	0

Task 4

(a)

Cost driver – per production set-up £	1,600	
Cost driver – per requisition £	1,000	
	Eff £	**Gee £**
Total production set-up cost	80,000	160,000
Set-up cost per unit	3.20	20.00
Total materials handling cost	240,000	120,000
Materials handling cost per unit	9.60	15.00

(b)

Budgeted labour hours	60,000	
Overhead absorption rate £	10	
	Eff £	**Gee £**
Overheads per unit	20.00	12.50
Total overheads absorbed	500,000	100,000

(c)

	Eff £	**Gee £**
Total cost per unit using ABC	62.80	75.00
Total cost per unit using absorption costing	70.00	52.50

(d)

The total cost of each product using overheads absorbed on a budgeted labour hour basis will be affected by the arbitrary nature of that system.

Product Eff will be considered more expensive to produce than if the costs were based on the more accurate ABC, and product Gee will be thought to be cheaper. This could result in poor decisions being made relating to (for example) product pricing, production scheduling, and product viability.

Task 5

(a)

	Units	Price/cost	Total £
Additional revenue	3,000,000	£0.10	300,000
Savings on materials	3,000,000	£0.15	450,000
Reduction in selling and distribution costs			150,000
Additional depreciation			(400,00)
Additional annual profit			500,000

(b)

Return on additional investment (%)	12.5
Total fixed costs	£1,350,000
Contribution per unit	£1.35

(c)

Technique	✔
Activity Based Costing	
Standard Costing Variance Analysis	
Discounted Cash Flow Net Present Value	✔
Trend Analysis with Seasonal Variations	

Task 6

(a)

Year	Cash Inflow £000	Cash Outflow £000	Net Cash Flow £000	Discount Factor	Present Value £000
0	0	400	−400	1.000	−400
1	0	400	−400	0.909	−364
2	0	1,340	−1,340	0.826	−1,107
3	6,000	3,340	2,660	0.751	1,998
4	7,500	4,140	3,360	0.683	2,295
5	4,200	1,740	2,460	0.621	1,528
	Totals		6,340		3,950

(b)

Situation	More Viable	Less Viable
Cost of capital is lower than 10%	✔	
Development costs are greater than £1,200,000		✔
Increased competition affects sales volume		✔
Product life cycle is extended, and additional sales are generated in year 6	✔	
Product becomes obsolete more quickly than planned		✔
Increased competition affects selling price		✔
Cost of capital is greater than 10%		✔

Task 7

(a)

	Eye Ltd	Jay plc
Selling price per unit	£9.00	£8.80
Direct material cost per unit	£2.00	£2.10
Direct labour cost per unit	£1.80	£1.75
Fixed production overheads per unit	£1.25	£1.38
Gross profit margin	43.89%	40.52%
Operating profit margin	12.08%	10.10%
Administration cost as % of turnover	9.03%	8.39%
Return on capital employed	6.69%	6.08%

(b)

Eye Ltd is generally performing well in comparison with its competitor, Jay plc. Eye is able to sell its products at a slightly higher unit price than Jay. However, Jay has a substantially higher volume of sales, and this may be partly the result of its lower selling price. Eye may wish to consider carrying out research to suggest ways that its sales volume could be increased.

Eye's costs of production per unit are lower than Jay's and this results in a higher gross profit margin. The only element of production cost where Eye compares unfavourably with Jay is the labour cost per unit, and it would be useful to examine this issue in more detail. If Eye's sales volume were to increase then its fixed costs would be spread over more units, further improving gross profit.

The non-production overheads for Eye are lower in total than those of Jay, but it should be remembered that Jay is supporting a higher sales volume. Both companies' non-production overheads account for a little over 30% of sales revenue, and therefore the higher gross profit margin of Eye is carried into a higher operating profit margin.

Analysis of administration costs per unit shows that Eye's costs are higher than Jay's. It would be useful to extend this analysis to other costs, to identify where any action may be appropriate.

Eye Ltd also has a higher return on capital employed than Jay plc, showing that it is utilising its assets effectively. Any action that Eye is able to take to increase its sales volume and / or reduce its costs would result in improved profitability using this and other indicators.

Task 8

(a)

	March	April	May
Actual price	£1.30	£1.25	£1.10
Trend	£1.28	£1.30	£1.32
Seasonal variation	+£0.02	−£0.05	−£0.22

(b)   **£14,825**

Workings: y − (£25 x 33) + £14,000

(c)

Month	Sales volume	3 month moving average
January	57,000	
February	58,000	57,500
March	57,500	58,500
April	60,000	59,500
May	61,000	60,500
June	60,500	61,500
July	63,000	

for your notes

for your notes

for your notes

for your notes

for your notes

for your notes

for your notes

for your notes

for your notes